W9-BCB-410

AMERICAN ANTIQUES
from
ISRAEL SACK COLLECTION

VOL. 4

HIGHLAND HOUSE PUBLISHERS INC.

Library of Congress Catalogue Card Number 76-10283

International Standard Book Number 0-918712-00-10

Printed in the United States of America

RHODE ISLAND

NEWPORT, RHODE ISLAND

PROVIDENCE, RHODE ISLAND

VIRGINIA

CABINETMAKERS

CLOCKMAKERS

SILVERSMITHS

PAINTERS

REGIONAL

FORM

Introduction

Volume Four brings together five hundred American decorative art objects. Twenty-one pages of color described by Antiquarian Albert Sack.

The color illustrations show the beauty of American woods, finishes and the work of the artist-craftsmen. Mr. Sack has forty-seven years of experience in acquiring and furnishing great works of decorative art to collectors and museums. His dedication and expertise have benefitted America's museums, private collectors and students.

I have purposely not incorporated the original documentation of furniture and decorative art objects into a continuous text. The reasoning is that the four volumes of American Antiques do provide a valuable, easy to use reference of 2,000 objects, fully documented, illustrated and indexed in a permanent form.

The publication of the fourth volume of the Israel Sack Collection approaches the celebration of our country's bicentennial. This historic event is being marked by a series of celebrations, some of which will feature the treasures of our artistic craftsmen's creations. These works are synonymous with the spirit of independence and liberty which our forefathers nurtured, and as works of art they are the living testament to these stalwart qualities which made our nation great.

Our job now is to keep our nation great. In rededicating ourselves to this task it is good to review and ponder somewhat on the sidelines to get a clearer perspective. The study and enjoyment of our great craftsmen's works gives us an opportunity to see and touch these symbols. Somehow there is a security to them that gives us the impetus to associate ourselves with their presence. The message comes through loud and clear.

It is with hope and faith and trust in our country's future that we dedicate this volume. For in turning to the past that which survives all the turbulence is what we can count on for the days ahead.

Joseph H. Hennage
Highland House Publisher Inc.

P3577 Chippendale mahogany tall clock with block and shell carved center door, flanked by fluted quarter columns, panelled base with chamfered and lamb's tongue corners, ogee bracket feet, broken arch top with rare spiral carved capitals in punchwork background, original stop fluted flame finials enamelled dial, superb golden brown patina, Goddard-Townsend, Newport, Rhode Island, circa 1760-1780.

Ht. 94½″ Wd. 18″ Dp. 9½″

P3755 Chippendale secretary desk with block and shell carved doors, fashioned of "plum pudding" mahogany, the desk section with blocked and shell carved interior and scooped pigeonhole drawers closely related to the interior of our labelled John Townsend desk (Vol. III, page 790) with a sliding well in the fallboard, original pine tree brasses and side carrying handles; the top drawer has two sliding wooden bolts, a feature seen on a labelled Townsend desk; ogee bracket feet; the upper section has two beautifully modelled block and shell carved doors flanked by deeply inset fluted quarter columns, the doors enclose an intricate fitted interior of vertical and horizontal partitions, closed bonnet top with bold inner mouldings and centered by a powerful fluted flame carved finial. The beauty of this superbly proportioned masterpiece is enhanced by a golden patina mellowing the drama of the plum pudding mottled figure. Attributed to John Townsend, Newport, Rhode Island, circa 1760-1770.

Ht. 8′2″ Wd. 40½″ Op. 23¾″ Wt. Level 30½″

853

P3448 Chippendale mahogany blo front slant top desk with block a shell carved lid, three drawers, og bracket feet with C-scrolled margin carving, the interior with convex a concave blocked drawers and scoop pigeonhole drawers, the center do with concave shell and cross-hatch center, the end top drawers sh carved with incised line borders, ri dark brown patina; bearing the orig nal label "John Townsend, Rho Island 1765." This desk descended the Townsend family and was pu chased by us from a direct descendar

A block and shell bureau in th Metropolitan Museum bears a close similar label by John Townsend in th same year.

Ht. 42″ Wd. 42″ Dp. 23″
Writing Level 30½″

1352 Chippendale mahogany bonnet top highboy with open claw feet, shell carved center apron, panelled scrollboard and rear dustboard, in superb state of preservation with beautiful golden brown patina, original brasses and finial, made by one of the Goddard-Townsend master craftsmen; Newport, R.I. circa 1750-1760.

The highboy and pocketbook were purchased from descendants of Christopher Lawton of South Kingston, R.I. b. 1728 d. 1752—married 1751 to Elizabeth Tripp. Elizabeth Tripp married (second time) 1775 to William Browning of South Kingston. The initials on the purse clasp are WB for William Browning.

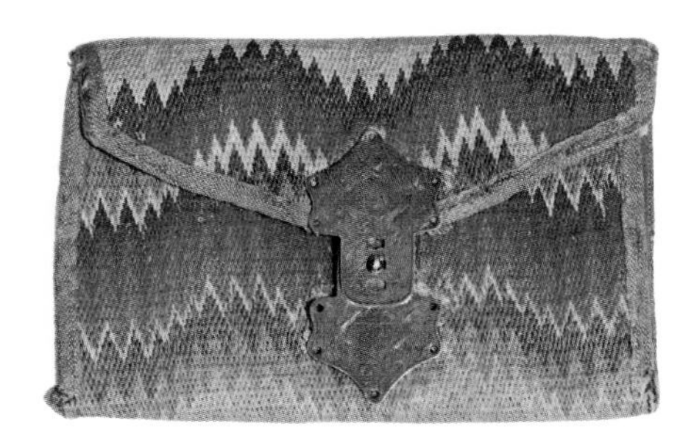

Ht. 7′1″ Wd. 39½″ Dp. 21¾″

Made by
John Townsend
Rhode Island
1765

P3685 Queen Anne walnut armchair. Crest rail centered by shell bordered by scrolled volutes, incurvature scooped arms ending in bold knuckle terminals, incurvature arm supports, horseshoe seat, cabriole legs with shell carved knees, stockinged feet, mellow brown original patina, Philadelphia circa 1740-1760. Descended in the Brown family of Marmora Township, New Jersey.

Ht. 42″ Wd. (across arms) 31¾″

Chippendale mahogany carved side chair. Descended from David Deshler, one of the first settlers in Germantown. Acquired by us from a descendant. Philadelphia circa 1760-1770.

P48 Chippendale mahogany blockfront chest-on-chest, the lower case with square blocking capped by rounded corners, bracket feet, the inner outline of which follows the line of the blocking, fan carved center pendant, the upper case with drawers flanked by fluted columns, the top row of drawers with fan carved center drawer and end drawers shaped to follow the line of the arch, bonnet top, original open flame carved finials with carved rims. This chest-on-chest is of rare narrow proportion accentuating the vertical emphasis. It retains the original brasses and a superb golden patina of great depth and mellowness. Attributed to Benjamin Frothingham, Charlestown, Massachusetts, circa 1760-1780.

Several characteristics of this piece are closely related to labelled Frothingham pieces and serve as the basis of the attribution: (1) the blocked bracket feet; (2) the shape of the blocking; (3) the open flame carved finials; (4) the shape of the arch; (5) the carved fan with thumbnail border. For an illustration of this piece, see ANTIQUES Magazine. November 1952, pages 392 to 395 and Frontispiece.

Descended in the family of Benjamin Hall who married Hepzibah Jones in Medford, Massachusetts, in 1752.

Ht. 7′6″ Wd. 42½″

P3926 Hepplewhite mahogany camel back sofa, sweeping serpentine curved back and seat with flaring rolled arms, line inlaid tapered legs ending in spade feet hewn from the solid with a mellow brown patina. H stretchers, New York circa 1780-1790. Descended in the family of Henry Rutgers, founder of Rutgers University.

Ht. 40″ Wd. 7′9¼″ Dp. 38″

No. 843 Chippendale Bombé desk of superbly figured solid San Domingan mahogany and important original brasses; branded on back—G. Cade—probably the maker, Boston, Mass. circa 1760-1770. Descended from Sylvanus Plympton of Woburn, Mass. who attended Harvard University in 1780. Illustrated in Frontispiece of Antiques Magazine of January 1941.

Ht. 42″ Wd. 42″ Dp. 25″ Wr. Lev. 30¾″

P3394 Queen Anne walnut block front lowboy, Boston, Mass., circa 1735-1745. This masterpiece of the block front form falls into the earliest block front group and is the rarest of the major block front designs. We know of two closely similar examples, almost certainly by the same unidentified maker. One, which belonged to a direct descendant of Priscilla Alden is illustrated in "Fine Points of Furniture, Early American" page 193. The other, formerly owned by Mrs. Charles Hallam Keep is privately owned. A squared block example, closely related to these is in the Henry F. du Pont Winterhur Museum, illustrated Downs Plate #325.

862

No. 656 Queen Anne cherry bonnet top highboy of exceptional grace, distinctive carved fans with convex shell centers, sunburst fan in scrollboard with conical center motif; mellow color. Connecticut circa 1740-1760.

Ht. 7′2″ Wd. 40″ Dp. 18″

Exhibited Pl. #84 Connecticut 17th & 18th Century Furniture, Wadsworth Atheneum, Hartford, Conn. 1967.

P3921 Chippendale mahogany blockfront bureau, finely sculptured claw and ball feet with swept back talons, scrolled center pendant, graduated drawers with round blocking retaining the original pine tree brasses, escutcheons, and side carry handles, Boston, Massachusetts, or vicinity, circa 1760-1780. The original warm golden brown patina, the undisturbed original condition and aspect of this bureau will satisfy the most discriminating connoisseur. This bureau formerly belonged to Mrs. Bradlee Smith of Brookline, Massachusetts, a direct descendant of William Penn.

Ht. 33¼″ Wd. 38″ Dp. 21¾″

P3855 Chippendale mahogany card table, frame and conforming top with blocked center and squared corners, superbly modelled squared cabriole legs with broad leaf and floral carving, open talon claw and ball feet with high ridged ankles, both rear legs pivot, choice original golden patina, attributed to John Townsend, Newport, Rhode Island, circa 1760-1765.

This table descended in the Lyman family of Boston and Newport. It was purchased by us from the estate of a descendant.

Ht. 27½″ Wd. 34½″ Dp. 17″

No. 458 Chippendale walnut scroll top highboy with shell and fine carved center drawers, original flame finials and carved rosette terminals. Philadelphia circa 1760. An important example purchased from the descendants of a prominent Philadelphia settler who came to Pennsylvania with William Penn. A family letter accompanies the piece. This is one of the few Philadelphia highboys with a truly graceful stance, overcoming the ponderousness of base prevalent in even some of the more highly carved specimens.

Ht. 93″ Wd. 44″ Dp. 23″

P3649 Sheraton mahogany breakfront bookcase, the upper section with glass doors of narrow Gothic panels formed by 48 panes of glass virtually all of which are original and intact, cyma curved shaped crest; the lower case is centered by a hinged desk drawer with 2 drawers below and an arched apron; the stiles are inlaid with a rare variation of the bellflower pattern with the flowers in black joined by white ovoid pellets; the case is supported by bulbous ring turned feet; the vertical effect is created by the flaming crotch figured veneer and the tight knit Gothic glass mullions; the beauty is enhanced by a superb bronze patina, Salem, Massachusetts, circa 1800-1810.

Ht. 91½″ Wd. 71½″ Dp. 20″

P3971 Sheraton mahogany and flame satinwood sewing table, rectangular shaped case with turret ends, the case containing two drawers in front and sewing slide at side, the drawer fronts, turret corners and twin panelled sides have beautifully figured flame satinwood veneer with crossbanded and inlaid borders, the edge bordered by lunette inlay; the conforming top is veneered with a burl center panel, with curly maple and blistered exotic wood and inlaid borders, the exquisitely delicate reeded legs with bulbous and ring turned capitals are typical of a group of related tables by John Seymour. The mellow original patina of the table is superb. Boston, Massachusetts circa 1800-1810. Ex Collection, the late Mitchel Taradash, illustrated ANTIQUES June 1946, page 360.

Ht. 30″ Top 21¼″ x 17″

Hepplewhite mahogany card table of dramatic reverse serpentine outline, attributed to Michael Allison, New York, circa 1796-1800. The central eagle panel with 16 stars is identical to that on a labelled Allison bureau in the Metropolitan Museum.

P3388 Hepplewhite mahogany tambour sideboard of rare small size bearing all the characteristics of the work of John Seymour and Son, i.e., the ivory escutcheon in the scrolled center bracket containing a lock to lock the tambours, the scrolled corner brackets and the inlaid columnar pilasters flanking the tambour shutters, and traces of the distinctive blue-green paint in the cupboard compartments. The top drawers also contain oval ivory escutcheons. The legs are tapered with banded cuffs and additional taper below; the carefully selected mahogany has taken on a satiny bronze patina typical of the Seymour shop. Attributed to John Seymour and Son, Boston, Massachusetts, circa 1790-1800.

Ht. 40½" Wd. 48½" Dp. 22¾"

Banjo clock made by Simon Willard of Boston, Massachusetts. Circa 1800.

This superb example with rare blue painted dial was sold a generation ago by Israel Sack.

P3744 Hepplewhite mahogany D shaped sideboard, serpentine center long drawer with floral urn in satinwood panel flanked by two small drawers, recessed center cupboard compartment flanked by convex turrets and bottle drawers which retain the original blown glass decanters; the legs and stiles are fronted by satinwood panels with oval inlaid urns flanking the drawers, top bordered by spiral inlay, original octagonal brasses, superb mellow brown patina, New York circa 1780-1800. The grace and delicacy attained in a sideboard of this length shows the hand of a master designer. It is, to our knowledge, the only sideboard to retain its original decanters.

Ht. 41½" Wd. 6'11½" Dp. 28"

P3489 Queen Anne walnut wing chair, superbly modelled cabriole legs with rare scrolled knee brackets enhanced by a golden patina; the masterful lines and powerful curves are accentuated by the undulating sides of the seat frame, a feature rarely found in a New England wing chair, Newport, Rhode Island, circa 1740-1760. We consider this example to be a masterpiece of the unadorned New England Queen Anne form.

Ht. 48″ Wd. 36″ Dp. 31″

Beating the Game

In our experience there has never been a successful collection formed without the guidance of a top flight dealer, either in the capacity of adviser or as a direct source of supply and outright purchase.

The value of the professional is threefold: (1) to judge authenticity, (2) to judge quality, and (3) to determine value.

The ability to judge quality and to determine value is predicated not only on his innate good judgment and taste but also on the range of objects he has seen and compared.

Rating an antique as to its comparative quality can only be judged against the whole panorama of the field. Attempting to compare it to illustrated examples covers only a small portion of extant pieces. Our photographic files and the thousands of examples we have handled over 60 years of specialization gives us a panorama which has vital significance. Furthermore pricing based on quality and authenticity is measured by an active marketing experience.

Comparing prices by form and type alone can be very misleading. There is a tremendous price range between an exceptional example of a particular form and an average example. We have seen many of our customers hopelessly overpay for an average example by comparing its lower price elsewhere to one of our top drawer pieces.

For some strange reason the very executive who would not think of making a judgment without the advice of either a top tax man, accountant or legal counsellor in his own field will blithely enter a strange field and attempt to beat the expert at his own game. This of course may be fun and recreation at low level prices, but in today's current market, the price of this challenge can become extremely costly.

HAROLD SACK ALBERT M. SACK ROBERT M. SACK

P3228 Early maple low post bed with the original brick red paint, head and foot posts with bottle turned legs and flattened ball terminals, original rails and shaped pine headboard, Massachusetts circa 1720-1740.

Ht. headposts 31″ Lg. 73½″ Wd. 44¾″
Ht. footposts 23″

Ht. 29¼″ Wd. 35¾″ Dp. 17⅝″

P3547 Early walnut small tavern table with one drawer, bulbous and ring turned legs with ball feet intact, old or original patina of depth and mellowness, Pennsylvania circa 1720-1740.

Ht. 29½″ Wd. 29″ Dp. 22½″

P3543 Chippendale tulip-poplar pencil post bed retaining the original blue green paint; the head and foot posts taper to a rare thinness at the top of ⅜ of an inch; the peaked headboard and footboard have cyma curved ends, the pillow boards are replaced but the evidence of their original presence offers a rare variation, the tester frame and the rails are original and also retain the blue green paint; the rails retain the original hand wrought iron bed bolts, Pennsylvania circa 1740-1770.

One of the finest pencil post beds in any museum or private collection.
Ht. 6′4″ Lg. 6′3″ Wd. 50½″

P3621 Sheraton birch field bed with the original bowed tester, shaped pine headboard and rails; retains the original brown patina, the foot posts are of rare excellence with slender bulbous reeding above a reeded urn, with an interesting pear shaped terminal and turned feet intact, octagonal tapering headposts, Salem, Massachusetts, circa 1800-1810. The long rails have a piece inserted to lengthen them and a corresponding piece inserted in the bowed canopy.

Ht. 86″ Lg. 6′9¾″ Wd. 53¼″

P3602 Hepplewhite cherry bow front bureau, the drawers, top edge and bracket feet are bordered by alternating black and white diagonal inlay, beautiful amber patina, Hartford, Connecticut, or Providence, Rhode Island, circa 1790-1810.

The inlaid borders and modified bracket feet are related to the secretary-desk illustrated "American Furniture, The Federal Period" by Montgomery plate 177.

Ht. 35″ Wd. 40½″ Dp. 22″

P3646 Chippendale mahogany bow front bureau of rare small size, ogee bracket feet, the drawers are veneered in a carefully chosen crotch pattern that alternates left and right, ogival moulded top which extends in back in a curved arc, choice color, Philadelphia circa 1780-1790. This bureau descended in the family of Robert Morris and may have been fashioned for an oval room in his country home, Fairmount Park.

Ht. 34¾″ Wd. 34″ Dp. 25″

P3610 Hepplewhite mahogany corner washstand, line inlaid outsplayed legs joined by pierced stretcher with dish rimmed disc center, bowed case containing small drawer and inlaid borders, scalloped apron above, choice brown patina, attributed to William Hook, Salem, Massachusetts, circa 1800-1810.

A washstand of the same form made by William Hook for his sister is in the Museum of Fine Arts, Boston, see Randall "American Furniture" plate 101.

Ht. 40½″ Wd. 21½″ Dp. 15″

P3619 Pilgrim maple slat back side chair with old black paint, finely turned ball finials, double sausage turned frontal stretchers, feet intact, Massachusetts circa 1680-1720.

Ht. 45¼″

P3572 Maple slat back armchair, five bent serpentine graduated slats, ball and ring turned center stretcher, exceptional full length ball turned feet, Pennsylvania circa 1730-1760.

Ht. 47¾″ Wd. 21½″

P3666 Assembled pair of Queen Anne maple side chairs, Spanish feet, rush seats, moulded stiles and horned yoke crests, mellow color, one chair of darker tone, Massachusetts circa 1730-1750. The turned side stretchers are characteristic of Andover and vicinity.

Ht. 41¼″

P3596 Queen Anne walnut side chair, stockinged drake feet, scrolled apron, vase shaped splat with high plinth, serpentine crest with scribed line borders, beautiful golden patina, school of William Savery, Philadelphia circa 1740-1760.

Ht. 39½″

P3588 Sheraton mahogany armchair, rectangular back with flaring stiles, three arrow shaped splats with fan carved terminals, rectangular fluted crest panel, tapered legs with spade feet, New York circa 1800. The mate to this chair from the collection of R. T. Haines Halsey is illustrated #188 in the Hudson-Fulton Exhibition catalogue, 1909, Metropolitan Museum of Art.

Ht. 36″ Wd. 24″

P3558 Chippendale walnut side chair, beautifully wrought strapwork splat with inverted heart center and smaller heart silhouette below crest flanked by scrolls, serpentine crest centered by webbed shell bordered by scrolls, the finely modelled cabriole legs have webbed shell carved knees and sculptured claw and ball feet, ruddy brown patina, Philadelphia circa 1750-1770.

Ht. 40¼″

P3553 Set of 6 Chippendale walnut claw and ball foot side chairs, carved shell centering aprons, interlaced splats with scrolled terminals, finely shaped crests centered by cabachon carved center shells and vigorous scrolled knuckle ear terminals, choice mellow brown patina, Philadelphia circa 1750-1770.

The chairs are not all of the same set with only slight variations.

Ht. 41½″

P3585 Chippendale mahogany armchair of tall stately proportion, interlaced Gothic splat with carved diamond center motif, scrolled ears, fluted stiles, finely shaped knuckle arms and serpentine arm supports, acanthus carved knees and brackets, apron centered by asymmetrical carved center, fine bronze color, Philadelphia circa 1760-1770.

Exhibited in Metropolitan Museum 1963 "American Art from American Collections," illustration #10 in the catalogue.

Ht. 41¼″

P3598 Pair of Hepplewhite mahogany heart back side chairs; the inlaid backs are of rare or unique design, the slats radiating from black and white sunburst inlaid crescents, the center with sunburst and half fan paterae, the flanking bowed slats with silhouetted hearts and fishtail scrolls, fluted back supports, ovoid stump rear legs, serpentine seat, tapered bellflower inlaid legs ending in modified spade feet, Boston, Massachusetts, circa 1780-1800. The distinctive foot is seen on a number of pieces by John Seymour.

Ht. 39¼″

P3559 Pair of Classical mahogany side chairs with superbly carved eagle splats, moulded stiles and legs, panelled crests, old crusty finish, attributed to Duncan Phyfe, New York circa 1810-1820. The later needlepoint seat covers bear the coat of arms of the Breese family of New York.

Ht. 33¾″

P3557 Chippendale mahogany Martha Washington or lolling chair the scooped arm has rare pinwheel carving and reeded outer edge, moulded arm supports and moulded tapered legs, original finish and linen undercover, Massachusetts circa 1770-1780. The chair has lost an 1½ inch height, the casters are a later addition. An example of this form is in the Taradash collection.

Ht. 41¾″ Wd. 25″ Dp. 28½″

P3561 Chippendale cherry tripod candlestand with rare sliding candle drawer, square top, finely turned urn column, amber color, Connecticut circa 1760-1780.

Ht. 26½″, Top 17¾″ by 18¼″

P3563 Assembled pair of Sheraton mahogany Martha Washington armchairs or lolling chairs, bulbous ring turned castered legs, moulded arm supports with moulding continuing to turnings, serpentine arms and crest, Salem, Massachusetts, or Portsmouth, New Hampshire, circa 1800-1810. The chairs have minor variations but are unquestionably by the same maker.

Left chair: Ht. 43¼″ Wd. 26½″

Right chair: Ht. 44¾″ Wd. 26½″

P3637 Decorated iron tray depicting the death of General Wolfe in the Battle of Quebec. The scene is after the famous painting of this subject by Benjamin West. The village of Pontypool in Wales excelled in the art of decorated iron ware and trays depicting American historic scenes emanated from this center from the Revolutionary era through the War of 1812. A similar tray is shown in Antiques August 1949, pg. 114. English circa 1780-1820.

Lg. 28½″ Wd. 22″ Ht. 1⅝″

P3590 Queen Anne walnut wing chair, boldly curved cabriole legs with pointed knees, arrow turned stretchers, flaring vertical roll arms and bold serpentine crest, mellow patina, Massachusetts circa 1750-1770. The compact scale adds to the appeal of the fine design.

Ht. 45½″ Wd. 36½″ Dp. 31″

P3564 Bone ship model with three masts and full rigging, two decks of guns, figurehead of lady in front, done by French prisoners of war in British prisons, English early 19th century.

Ht. (case) 16½″ Lg. (case) 21½″ Dp (case) 7¾″

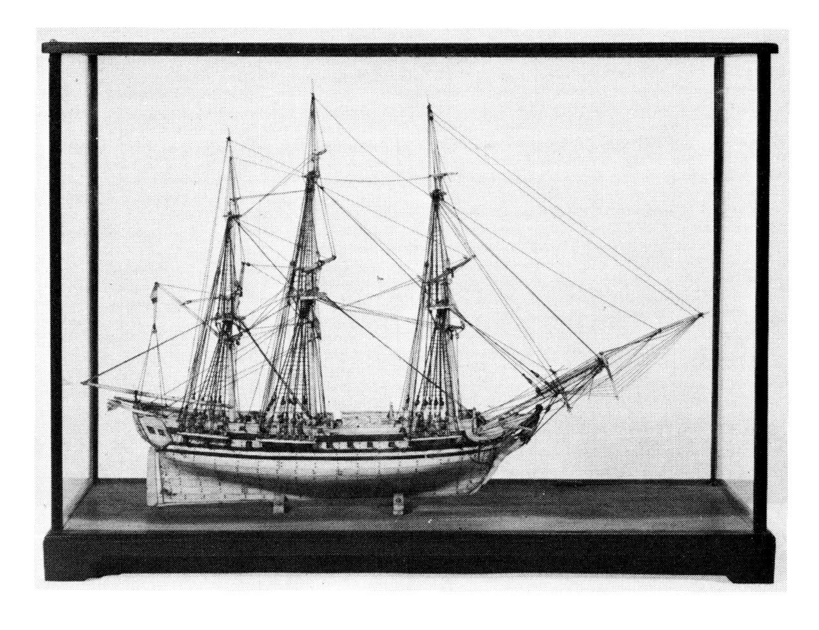

P3503 Queen Anne walnut wing chair, typical Philadelphia form with bowed seat frame, pillow roll arms with boldly flaring arms, cabriole legs with platformed disc pad feet, golden color, dramatically raking profile, Philadelphia circa 1740-1760. While this form of wing chair gained wide popularity in the Chippendale period, only a handful of Queen Anne examples are known.

Ht. 47½″ Wd. 35½″ Dp. 30″

Timothy Danielson was a major-general in the Revolution. He was a leader in molding public opinion before the Revolution as an active member of the provincial Congresses and as a representative to the General Court. He was Chief Justice of the Court of Common Pleas for Hampshire County and a member of the Convention which framed the Massachusetts State Constitution.

Owners of Wing Chair

1. General Timothy Danielson, Born Dec. 6, 1733.
2. Sarah Danielson, Born 1790; Died Aug. 10, 1830.
3. Francis Danielson Lincoln, Born Sept. 30, 1821; Died May 8, 1901.
4. Henrietta Lincoln Peirce, Born July 2, 1853; Died January 18, 1902.
5. Charles Lincoln Peirce, Born April 11, 1881; Died May 27, 1945.
6. Ronald Webster Lincoln Peirce, Born June 27, 1904; Died June 22, 1965.

P3587 Chippendale mahogany wing chair, bowed seat frame with rounded corners, cabriole legs with claw and ball feet, turned stretchers and chamfered rear legs, original mellow brown finish, Massachusetts circa 1760-1770. This chair descended in the family of General Timothy Danielson of Brimfield, Massachusetts. It is illustrated in Antiques Magazine December 1930 while still in the possession of the family.

Ht. 45¾″ Wd. 34¾″ Dp. 31″

P3570 Hepplewhite mahogany wing chair, horizontal sloping roll arms, bowed crest, moulded tapered legs with raised cuffed feet, Baltimore, Maryland, circa 1780-1800. Secondary woods are hard pine, oak, and poplar.

Descended in the Scott family of Baltimore. The history that came with the chair reads as follows:

> "For #6 property of CFS and SRS.
> Hepplewhite easy chair. This particular chair was
> willed to Nellie Lewis by Martha Washington. Banded
> front legs. Baltimore *SCOTT* FAMILY.
> from Rosa Bott Eisenhart."

Ht. 48″ Wd. 34½″ Dp. 34½″

P3591 Chippendale mahogany chest on chest, broken arch top with floral carved terminals, original flame finials, fluted columns on upper case section, original brasses, bracket feet, base centered by fan carved pendant, Marblehead, Massachusetts, or vicinity circa 1760-1780.

Ht. 7½″ Wd. 42″ Dp. 21½″

P3656 Pair of leather decorated fire buckets with allegorical depictions of Mercury blowing trumpet, inscribed Nath'l B. Perkins, Active 1840.

Ht. 11½″ Diam. 8½″

P3632 Classical mahogany window seat, backs with imposed crests with floral carved ends, linenfold drapery splats, saber legs, original slip seat frame, faded light brown color, Boston, Massachusetts circa 1810-1820. A chair of related design from the John Hancock home is illustrated in "Furniture of the Olden Time" by Frances Clara Morse, page 267.

Ht. 34½″ Wd. 47¼″ Dp. 21½″

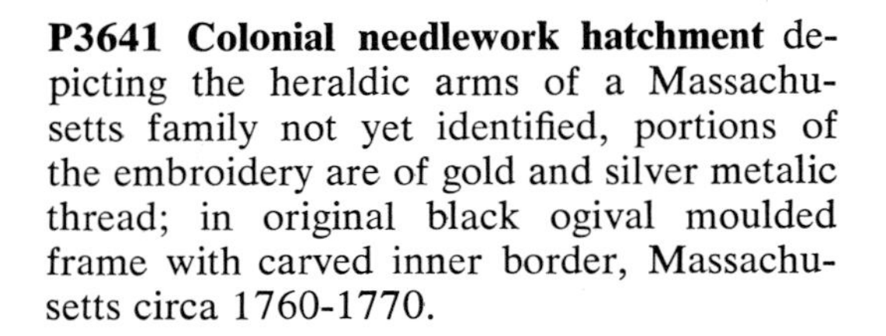

P3641 Colonial needlework hatchment depicting the heraldic arms of a Massachusetts family not yet identified, portions of the embroidery are of gold and silver metalic thread; in original black ogival moulded frame with carved inner border, Massachusetts circa 1760-1770.

Descended in the Hayden family of Boston, Massachusetts.

Ht. 22″ Wd. 19¼″

P3600 Chippendale San Domingan mahogany dropleaf dining table of important size, square fluted legs, choice color and craftsmanship, Newport, Rhode Island, circa 1760-1780.

Ht. 28″ Lg. 60″ Wd. (open) 59⅜″
Wd. (closed) 22″

GODDARD-TOWNSEND TALL CLOCK

P3577 Chippendale mahogany tall clock with block and shell carved center door, flanked by fluted quarter columns, panelled base with chamfered and lamb's tongue corners, ogee bracket feet, broken arch top with rare spiral carved capitals in punchwork background, original stop fluted flame finials enamelled dial, superb golden brown patina, Goddard-Townsend, Newport, Rhode Island, circa 1760-1780.

Ht. 94½″ Wd. 18″ Dp. 9½″

P3661 Hepplewhite mahogany D-shaped card table, the front centered by an oblong panel with beautiful inlaid Grecian urn in curly maple background in tooth inlaid border, the panels above each line inlaid leg contain oval inlaid shells in green background, fine brown color, Massachusetts circa 1780-1800. A finely inlaid sideboard labelled William Lloyd, Springfield, Massachusetts, has a closely related Grecian urn.

Ht. 29¼″ Wd. 35¼″
Dp. 17″

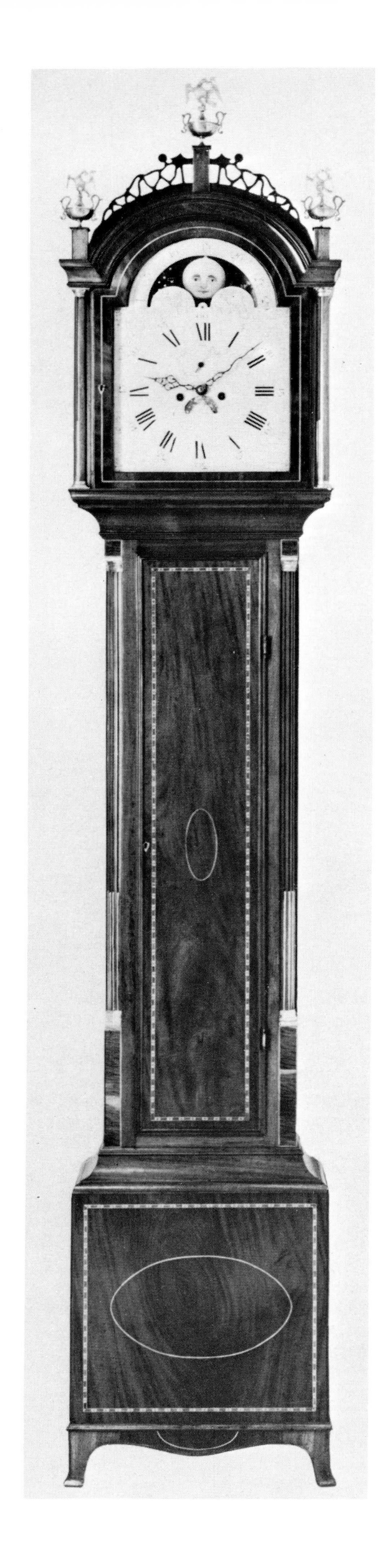

P3599 Hepplewhite mahogany tall clock, stately case of fine proportions and design, the base panel and moulded door with inlaid borders and oval centers, French feet and repeat inlaid semi-circle in apron, enamelled moon dial, original fretwork and superb original brass finials depicting dove of peace on elliptical urns with chased handles, choice nut brown color, Boston, Massachusetts, circa 1790-1800.

Ht. 9′2″ Wd. 19″ Dp. 9¼″

P3658 Chippendale cherry small slant top desk, stepped interior with two rows of drawers, the bottom row with ogival fronts, concave shell with scribed line border in top center drawer, ogee bracket feet, original large brasses with crescent cutouts, superb amber color, chestnut secondary, Newport, Rhode Island circa 1760-1780.

Ht. 42¾″ Wd. 36″ Dp. 19¾″ W.L. 30¾″

This desk was sold by us to a Connecticut collector in 1935. Our old photograph of the desk in our shop at 422 Madison Avenue 1935 is shown below. We have repurchased this desk for ten times the investment by its previous owner. In an appreciative letter to us he states:

"Your firm has maintained ever since that antiques were a sound investment. Certainly my experience is ample proof of that.

It has been a pleasure to do business with you."

P3601 Hepplewhite mahogany two drawer tambour desk, tapered line inlaid legs with additional taper below cuffs, the drawers with original chased brasses of cyma curved outline, the door of the tambour section centered by a beautiful inlaid urn, fine inlaid borders flanking door and bordering top, choice patina, Boston or Salem, Massachusetts, circa 1780-1800.

Ht. 44½″ Wd. 37″ Dp. 20″ W.L. ½″

P3657 Chippendale San Domingan mahogany slant top desk, bracket feet with scrolled inner outline, stepped interior, the upper row of drawers of blocked serpentine outline, centered by a row of three concave blocked drawers, the upper drawer with carved fan and flanked by pilastered document drawers, made and signed by Henry Rust, Salem, Massachusetts, 1770. The original writing and drawing on the document drawers illustrated not only establish Henry Rust as the maker of this desk in 1770 but also as a primitive artist and poet.

The inscription reads:

"This desk Made By Henry Rust of Salem
Salem, New England
One Thousand seven Hundred and Seventy."

Ht. 42″ Wd. 37″ Dp. 18½″ Wr. Lvl. 30″

INSCRIPTIONS ON DOCUMENT DRAWERS

Bottom inscription reads:
"Salem, New England
One Thousand Seven Hundred
and Seventy"

This Desk Made By
Henry Rust of Salem

P3664 Queen Anne walnut bonnet top highboy, cabriole legs ending in platformed wafer pad feet, the upper and lower case sections have bold fan carved center drawers, the upper fan carved drawer is flanked by end drawers with sides complementing the curve of the arch, mellow light brown patina, Boston, Massachusetts, or vicinity circa 1750-1760.

The highboy descended through the Edmands family of Boston. Fire buckets came from Catherine Barnes who married Major General Benjamin Franklin Edmands of Civil War fame. The highboy was in family of the Major General, then to Thomas Franklin Edmands-Horton Edmands-Thomas Horton Edmands. All resided in Boston. The highboy dates back in the Edmands family to the 18th century but ownership at that time is confused. A geneology of family is available through a family bible in Concord, Massachusetts.

Ht. 7′3½″ Wd. 41½″ Dp. 21¾″

P3668 Sheraton mahogany secretary-desk of rare small size, upper case with Gothic inlaid mullions, drawers, pigeonholes and shelves behind, lower case with slanting hinged lid one drawer, recessed cupboard section with two oval inlaid bowed doors, flanked by curly maple turrets, delicate tapered reeded legs, choice mellow brown patina, Boston or Salem, Massachusetts, circa 1800–1810.

Ht. (with gallery) 54″
Wd. 37¾″ Dp. 19¼″

P3620 Queen Anne cherry highboy, graceful cabriole legs with pointed knees and ridged knee returns ending in scrolled volutes, platformed wafer pad feet; the carved fan in lower case section is complemented by a smaller fan of same design centering the top drawer, original brasses, amber color, Salem, Massachusetts, circa 1750-1760.

Ht. 73″ Wd. 39½″ Dp. 20½″

P3608 Hepplewhite maple and pine corner washstand with original painted floral decoration with off white background, gray borders and panels, one drawer with original knob, Salem, Massachusetts, circa 1800-1810.

Ht. 41¾″ Wd. 23″ Dp. 15″

P3645 Queen Anne lowboy, crotch walnut veneered drawer fronts with herringbone borders, crotch walnut veneered top of quartered segments with herringbone and crossbanded borders, shaped apron with pointed arch center, original cock-beading and pendants, graceful cabriole legs ending in platformed pad feet, original engraved brasses, beautiful golden brown patina, Boston, Massachusetts, circa 1735-1750.

The lowboy belonged to Benjamin Lincoln 1733-1810 of Hingham, Massachusetts, a Major-General in the Revolutionary War. General Lincoln was put in command of the American forces defending the Southern states against General Cornwallis. He became Secretary of War for the Continental Congress and became the first Secretary of War of this country. His home is still standing in Hingham.

This lowboy descended in the Lincoln-Huntington family and was purchased from a direct descendant. A history by this descendant will be given to the purchaser.

Ht. 32″ Wd. 33¾″ Dp. 21½″

P3603 Queen Anne cherry lowboy, gracefully scrolled cyma curved apron, slender cabriole legs ending in stockinged drake feet with shell carved knees, moulded top with notched corners, amber color, South Jersey or Pennsylvania circa 1750-1760.

Ht. 30″ Wd. (top) 36″ Dp. (top) 23¾″

P3653 Queen Anne walnut lowboy of compact proportions with concave blocked scooped center drawer, moulded top with notched corners, light brown color, original brasses, Massachusetts circa 1740-1760.

Ht. 30″ Wd. (top) 33¾″ Dp. 20¼″

P3556 Queen Anne walnut mirror with original two section bevelled glasses, moulded ogival frame border with cyma curved upper outline with pointed center, carved and gilded inner border, rare carved and gilded elliptical shell in crest with peanut center, in the finest original state with original finish, gilt and back, American or English circa 1740-1760. Descended in a Boston family.

Ht. 41″ Wd. 16½″

P3629 Queen Anne walnut mirror with two section bevelled glasses, carved and gilded pierced cartouche with peanut center in crest, carved and gilded side leaves and mirror border, beautifuly scrolled and strapwork ears at crest and base, American or English circa 1740-1760.

A related mirror is shown in Lockwood "Colonial Furniture in America" 1926 Vol. 1, page 290 (supplement).

Ht. 49″ Wd. 24½″

P3582 Small Chippendale mirror with the original Japanned decoration, in original state including mirror glass and back, American or English circa 1760-1780.

Ht. 27¾″ Wd. 16″

P3638 Chippendale walnut mirror with scrolled crest and base, silhouetted gilded cartouche with peanut center in crest, concave gilded shell in base. The original mirrored glass has ogival moulded border with notched corners and carved and gilded inner border, American or English circa 1750-1770. This mirror is in mint untouched state with the original finish, gilt and black.

Ht. 42″ Wd. 22″

P3623 Chippendale carved and gilded overmantel mirror with superbly carved frame, in the finest original state retaining the original gilding, 3 sectioned mirror glass and back. English circa 1750-1770. While not of American manufacture it is the form of mirror likely to be found in a Philadelphia pre-Revolutionary mansion.

Ht. 21½″ Wd. 47½″

P3627 Queen Anne walnut mirror of important size, finely scrolled crest centered by pierced gilded shell, bold ogival mirror borders, fine mellow patina, the original two sectioned mirror glasses have been resilvered, American or English circa 1740-1760. The back is lined with New York newspaper of 1866.

Ht. 55½″ Wd. 20″

P3636 Chippendale walnut mirror with scrolled crest and base, carved and gilded silhouetted shell in crest, gilded side vines, cyma curved and leaf carved gilded mirror border and base, fine mellow brown patina, American or English circa 1750-1760.

Ht. 38″ Wd. 19¾″

P3640 Chippendale walnut mirror with scrolled crest and base, pierced gilded silhouetted shell in crest, American or English circa 1760-1780.

Ht. 37″ Wd. 19½″

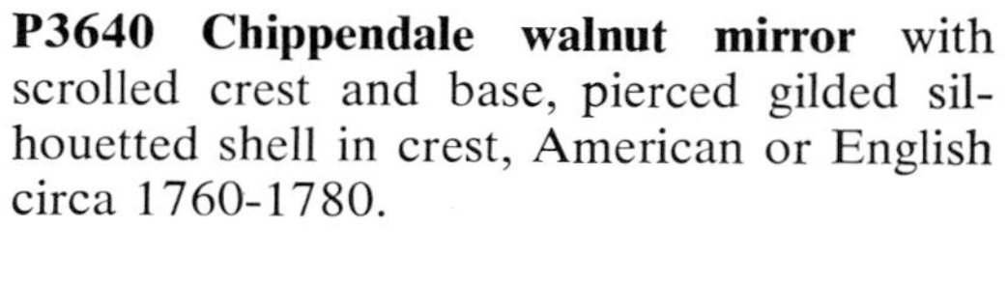

P3635 Chippendale walnut mirror, beautifully scrolled crest and base, concave gilded shell in crest, mellow light brown patina, American or English circa 1750-1770.

Ht. 34½″ Wd. 17½″

P3581 Hepplewhite mahogany mirror with broken arch top and crested by original carved and gilded eagle on spiral plinth, egg and dart carved and gilded mirror borders, of definite American origin and attributed to New York circa 1780-1800. A related mirror is illustrated in "American Furniture, The Federal Period" Montgomery, plate 217.

Ht. 51″ Wd. 23½″

A close affinity is apparent in the two mirrors on this page. Both have virtually identical sculptured eagles apparently by the same hand and related leaf carved mirror frames. The closeness of their dimensions and the fact the eagles face each other makes them ideal for use as a pair. They bear a close resemblance to the great convex mirror in the Museum of Fine Arts, Boston, illustrated "M. and M. Karolik Collection" plate 141.

P3616 Classical gilt convex mirror, circular moulded frame with leaf carved inner border and gilded balls, finely sculptured eagle perched on rocks with a single gilded ball suspended on chain from his beak, flanked by dolphins, four scrolled gilt wood brackets supporting candle sockets, Boston, Massachusetts, circa 1800-1810.

Descended in the Brooks family of Cambridge, Mass.

Ht. 45″ Wd. 25½″

P3617 Classical gilt convex mirror, circular moulded frame with leaf carved inner border and gilded balls, finely sculptured eagle perched on rocks, with drapery chains in his beak, four scrolled gilt wood brackets supporting candle sockets, Boston, Massachusetts, circa 1800-1810.

Descended in the Gray family of Boston.

Ht. 43″ Wd. 25½″

P3639 Two courting mirrors with eglomise glass centers and borders, European for the American market circa 1790-1818.

While not a matched pair, the mirrors are closely similar and serve as excellent companions.

Hts. 16″ & 15¾″ Wds. 11″ & 10¾″

P3642 Sheraton "Bilboa" mirror, sepia colored marble frame and columns with gilt borders, scrolled and floral gilded crest with fluted urn center, fine original aspect, Continental for the American market circa 1790-1800.

Ht. 30″ Wd. 14¼″

P3583 Sheraton gilt mirror with spiral borders, original eglomise glass panel depicting landscape in pastel colors, in exceptional state retaining the original gilding, Boston, Massachusetts circa 1800-1810.

Ht. 30½″ Wd. 14¾″

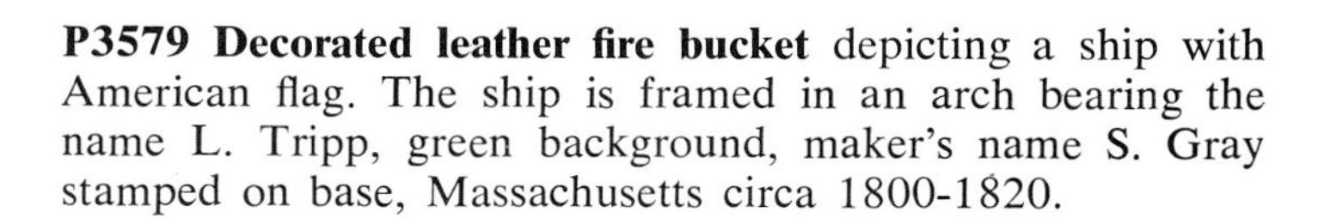
P3579 Decorated leather fire bucket depicting a ship with American flag. The ship is framed in an arch bearing the name L. Tripp, green background, maker's name S. Gray stamped on base, Massachusetts circa 1800-1820.

Ht. 13″ Diam. 8″

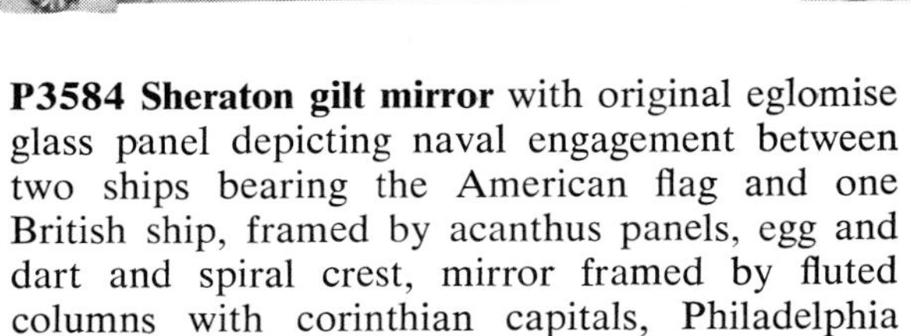

P3584 Sheraton gilt mirror with original eglomise glass panel depicting naval engagement between two ships bearing the American flag and one British ship, framed by acanthus panels, egg and dart and spiral crest, mirror framed by fluted columns with corinthian capitals, Philadelphia circa 1815-1820.

Ht. 31″ 17½″

P3625 Sheraton gilt mirror, original eglomise glass panel with cross hatched background and centering the American eagle and shield with 15 stars in brilliant colors, the original mirrored glass is flanked by reeded cluster columns with Corinthian capitals and acanthus plinths; the eglomise glass panel has vertical hair line cracks; Salem, Massachusetts, circa 1800-1815.

A closely related mirror with the rare eglomise eagle panel signed by Chadwick and Frye of Andover and Salem is shown in Sack Brochure #21, page 55, P3545. The two mirrors are virtually the same size and would serve as excellent companions.

Ht. 37¼″ Wd. 19″

P3618 Classical gilt convex mirror of important size, circular moulded frame with chain carved inner border and gilded balls, surmounted by beautifully sculptured black eagle on flaring leaf plinth, flanked by scrolled brackets, the base with two intertwined dolphins and four scrolled gilt candle brackets supporting candle sockets, attributed to John Doggett, Boston, Massachusetts, circa 1800-1810.

This mirror is not labelled. Yet comparison of this glass with the engraving on John Doggett's label shown below leaves no doubt to its authorship. Related are the intertwined dolphins; the distinctive plinths with flaring leaves and the broad leaf carved brackets.

Ht. 53″ Wd. 29″

JOHN DOGGETT,
Gilder,
Looking Glafs & Picture Frame
Manufacturer.
Roxbury.
Constantly for sale
a large afsortment of
Looking Glafses.

P3628 Large octagonal work box of bird's eye maple with curly maple top and base borders, lion ring side handles, fitted interior containing five compartments with covers, the covers of geometric shapes with tooled leather surfaces and ivory knobs, school of John and Thomas Seymour, Boston, Massachusetts, circa 1800-1814. The box bears the family plaque reading "Maria Gansevoort Melville from her father Thomas Melville, Oct. 1814."

Thomas Melville of Boston was a Major in the Revolution and a member of the Boston Tea Party. Maria Gansevoort was the daughter of General Peter Gansevoort of Albany, She married Allan Melville, son of Major Thomas Melville. They had two sons, Gansevoort and Herman. Herman Melville was the author of "Moby Dick."

A later plaque at base reads "Maria Gansevoort Melville June 10, 1874."

Ht. 5¼″ Wd. 14¼″ Dp. 10¼″

P3253 Chippendale mahogany bombé tea caddy, original escutcheon and bale handle, golden brown faded patina, white pine base board, Massachusetts circa 1760-1770. While English bombé tea caddies are not uncommon, an American example is a distinct rarity.

Ht. 7¼″ Wd. 10″ Dp. 5½″

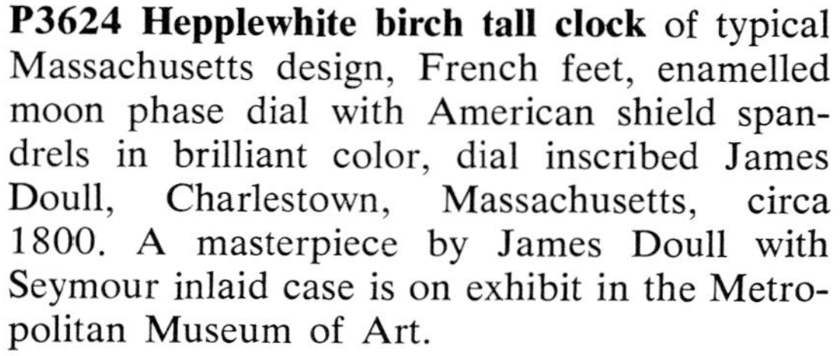

P3624 Hepplewhite birch tall clock of typical Massachusetts design, French feet, enamelled moon phase dial with American shield spandrels in brilliant color, dial inscribed James Doull, Charlestown, Massachusetts, circa 1800. A masterpiece by James Doull with Seymour inlaid case is on exhibit in the Metropolitan Museum of Art.

Ht. 7′6″ Wd. 19″ Dp. 10″

P3597 Hepplewhite mahogany secretary desk with tambour center section, two drawers in base section with original octagonal eagle brasses, the stiles have bellflower and a distinctive cross inlaid motif; upper section with small diamond panes; the interior of the upper case contains drawers and pigeonholes with a blue green painted background behind the shelves, superb mellow brown patina, Salem or Boston, Massachusetts, circa 1780-1800.

Ht. 7′7″ Wd. 39″ Dp. 21½″ Writing Ht. 29¾″

JONATHAN NICHOLS SECRETARY

P3555 Chippendale San Domingan mahogany secretary-desk, closed bonnet top of typical Newport design with divided panelled scrollboard, the inner arch bordered by finely wrought ogival mouldings in deep relief, original stop fluted finials, rectangular deeply chamfered door panels, ogee bracket feet, blocked and shell carved desk interior with scooped drawer pigeonhole terminals, upper interior with cyma scrolled vertical dividers, choice ruddy brown patina, ascribed to John Townsend Newport, Rhode Island, circa 1760-1770.

Ht. 8′2″ Wd. 40½″ Dp. 23″ Writing Ht. 31½″

This secretary descended from Jonathan Nichols (1770-1774) of Newport who owned the White Horse Tavern. It was purchased by us from a seventh generation descendant of Jonathan Nichols.

The family descent follows:
1. Jonathan Nichols 1700-1774
2. Walter Nichols 1748-1823
3. William Stoddard Nichols 1785-1871
4. Thomas Pitman Nichols 1816-1897
5. Othniel Foster Nichols 1845-1908

A letter from the descendant outlining this history and other related family documents will be given to the purchaser.

The relationship of the desk interior to that of our labelled John Townsend desk is remarkable. Following are illustrations of the two interiors for comparison.

P3555 Nichols secretary

P3448 Labelled John Townsend desk

The illustrations below compare the pigeonhole terminal drawers from the labelled Townsend desk and Nichols secretary.

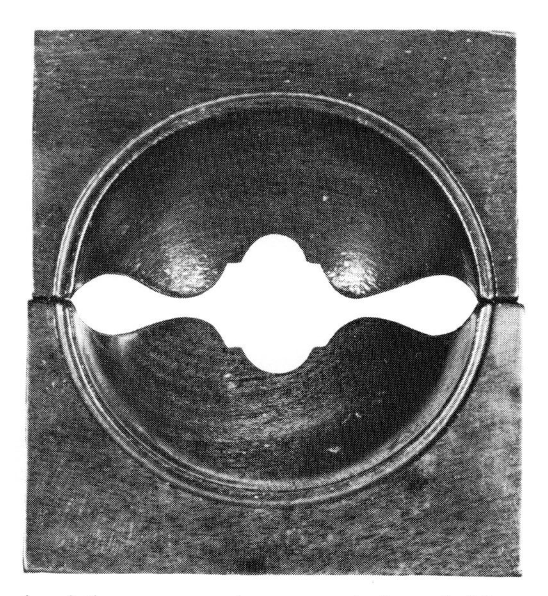

On the basis of these comparisons, ascription of this secretary to John Townsend is assured.

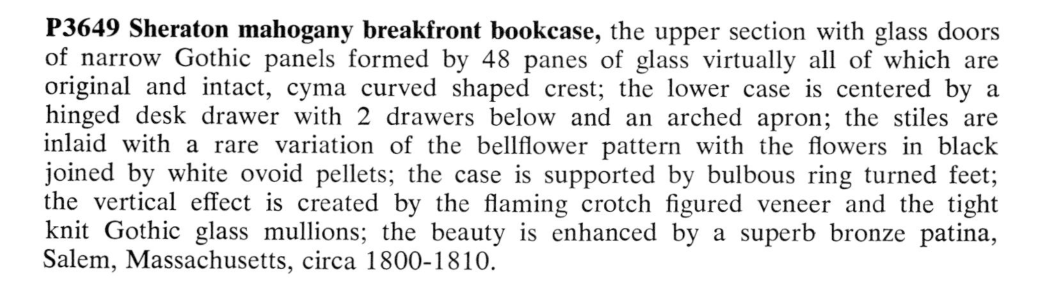

P3649 Sheraton mahogany breakfront bookcase, the upper section with glass doors of narrow Gothic panels formed by 48 panes of glass virtually all of which are original and intact, cyma curved shaped crest; the lower case is centered by a hinged desk drawer with 2 drawers below and an arched apron; the stiles are inlaid with a rare variation of the bellflower pattern with the flowers in black joined by white ovoid pellets; the case is supported by bulbous ring turned feet; the vertical effect is created by the flaming crotch figured veneer and the tight knit Gothic glass mullions; the beauty is enhanced by a superb bronze patina, Salem, Massachusetts, circa 1800-1810.

Ht. 91½″ Wd. 71½″ Dp. 20″

P563 Hepplewhite mahogany small sideboard with rare gallery top, line inlaid tapered legs and spade feet; the case is comprised of a top row of three drawers below which is a square center drawer and two cupboard compartments; the fronts are hinged by brass quadrants, each with inlaid sunburst paterae in larger ovals with checkered inlaid borders; the ovals contained in mitred panels with crossbanded borders; the sides have repeats of this design; the stiles with a chain inlaid design, the rarity of the design is enhanced by a superb brown patina of great depth and mellowness, attributed to Stephen Badlam, Dorchester (Boston), Massachusetts, circa 1790-1800.

Comparison of the paterae and wavy gallery with that on a tray stamped S. BADLAM, Benjamin Flayderman Sales, 1931, catalogue #82 supports the attribution.

Ht. 39″ Wd. 60″ Dp. 23½″

P3568 Hepplewhite mahogany bow back sofa with serpentine crest, seat and moulded arm supports, tapered castered legs, tulip-poplar frame, Maryland circa 1780-1800.

Ht. 37″ Wd. 80″ Dp. 28″

P3592 Pair of Queen Anne cherry side chairs with balloon seat frames, superbly modelled cabriole legs of smooth serpentine outline ending in pad feet, turned side stretchers and rear stretcher and vase shaped splats with peaked spurs, yoke shaped crest rails, chamfered rear legs, deep amber patina, Connecticut circa 1740-1760.

The chairs are of identical design to the great armchair that belonged to Governor Pitkin of Connecticut, illustrated catalogue "Connecticut Furniture" 1967 #232 and may be of that set.

Ht. 40½″

P3654 Rare Queen Anne San Domingan mahogany console table, finely modelled cabriole legs with slender ankles and platformed pad feet, quarter round apron moulding, moulded top with notched corners and retaining mouldings below, finished on all four sides, fine mellow brown color, Newport, Rhode Island, or Boston, Massachusetts, circa 1750-1760.

Ht. 31¼″ Wd. 47″ Dp. 23½″

P3368 Chippendale San Domingan mahogany sideboard table with Marlborough feet, original pierced corner brackets of strapwork design, two drawers, overhanging top with retaining moulding, fine mellow brown patina, Goddard-Townsend craftsmanship, Newport, Rhode Island, circa 1760-1770.

Descent:

1. James Birckhead married
   Eliza Hunter, grandaughter of Dr. William Hunter
2. Dr. William Birckhead married
   Sarah King, daughter of David King
3. Dr. David King, first President of the Newport Historical Society
4. Descended through the family to Mrs. Cabot Coville

The form to our knowledge is unique and represents a rare occurence of the Marlborough leg school in Newport.

Ht. 32″ Wd. 52″ Dp. 25″

P3567 Hepplewhite mahogany D-shaped card table or serving table of rare size, frame centered by raised rectangular panel framing a crotch veneered oval, crossbanded top and apron borders, beautiful nut brown patina, Boston, Massachusetts, circa 1780-1810. This table is 5½ inches wider than the standard card table, making it ideal for use as a serving table.

Ht. 29¾″ Wd. 41½″
Dp. 20½″

P3574 Chippendale mahogany card table with drawer at one end, beautiful serpentine shaped top with porringer corners, square legs with beaded corners, pierced brackets with circled centers, choice nut brown patina, Newport, Rhode Island, circa 1760-1780.

Ht. 29½″ Wd. 35¾″ Dp. 17⅝″

P3575 Sheraton mahogany serpentine shaped card table with turret corners, the frame contains three divided panels of curly satinwood with spiral inlaid borders, panels repeated on sides and turret corners, the bulbous turned reeded legs are of rare excellence, choice golden patina, Boston, Massachusetts, circa 1800-1810.

P3613 Chippendale walnut bureau of rare small size, fluted quarter columns, finely modelled platformed ogee bracket feet, the drawers and top are solid with fine figured grain and light brown color, Philadelphia circa 1760-1780.

Wd. (case) 31½″ Dp. (case) 19½″
Wd. (top) 33½″ Dp. (top) 20½″
Ht. 34″

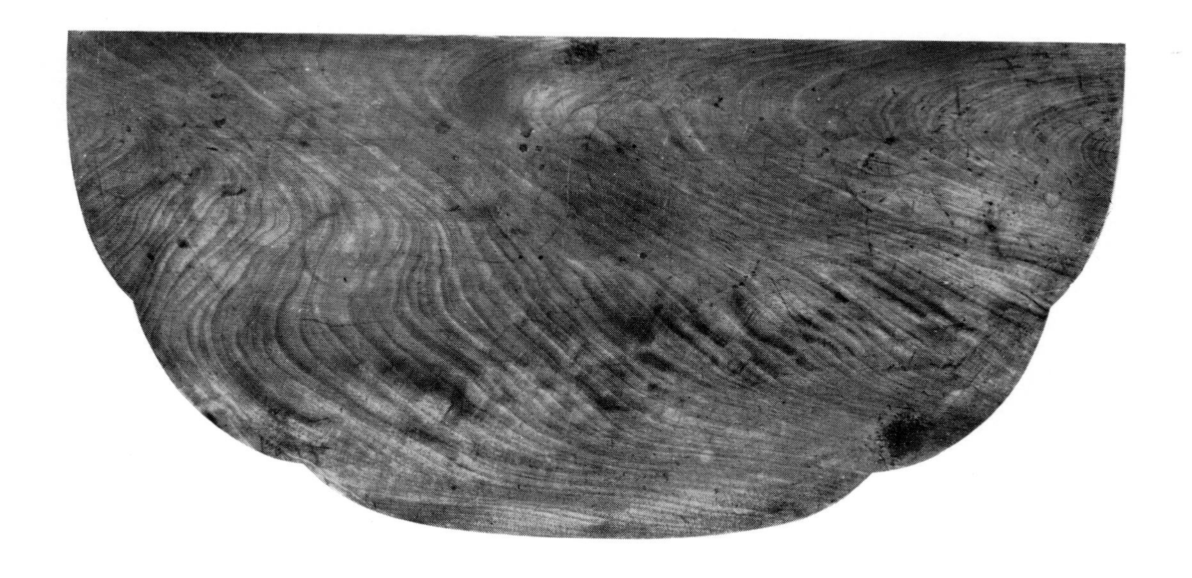

P3605 Pair of Sheraton mahogany five legged card tables; the five petalled clover leaf shape of the frames and conforming tops adds grace to the outline, choice crotch veneered frame, the fronts centered by rectangular crotch panels, slender reeded legs ending in bulbous feet, rich bronze patina, New York circa 1800-1810.

Ht. 29½″ Wd. 36″ Dp. 17¾″

P3560 Rare small Sheraton cherry two part dining table or breakfast table, two ovoid console ends with reeded edges each with a drop leaf; each section has two swing legs to support the leaves, slender tapered reeded legs with pear shaped castered feet, mellow light brown patina, Salem, Massachusetts, circa 1800-1810.

Ht. 30″ Lg. 69½″ Wd. 41¾″

P3569 Chippendale San Domingan mahogany tripod tip table with deep dish rim, finely turned ball and ring turned and bulbous column, cabriole legs with panelled sides ending in paw feet, maple block and cleats, Goddard-Townsend, Newport, Rhode Island, circa 1750-1770. The distinctive paw feet appear on a tripod table with a bill of sale of John Goddard, "Arts and Crafts of Newport" Carpenter plate #79.

Ht. 26¼″ Dia. 31¾″

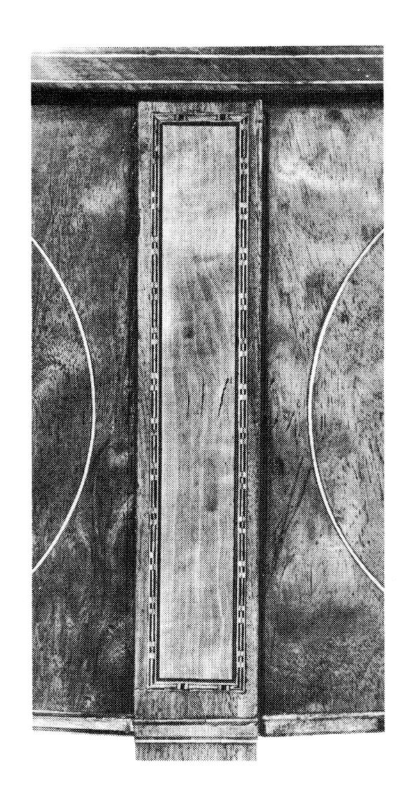

P3573 Hepplewhite mahogany "bandbox" work table, hinged top, oval inlaid panels on each case section with exceptional blistered crotch figured veneer, rectangular satinwood panels on stiles with inlaid borders, line inlaid tapered legs with banded cuffs, superb golden brown patina, Baltimore or Annapolis, Maryland, circa 1780-1800.

Ht. 30¼″ Wd. 22¾″
Dp. 15½″

P3550 Queen Anne mahogany dropleaf table, finely modelled cabriole legs with platformed pad feet, cyma curved scrolled apron, Salem, Massachusetts, circa 1740-1770.

Ht. 27¾″ Top 48″ by 48″
Wd. (closed) 17½″

P2484 Chippendale San Domingan mahogany card table with concave blocked front, cabriole legs, acanthus carved knees centered by a four petalled flower in punchwork background, finely sculptured claw and ball feet with swept back talons, Boston, Massachusetts, circa 1760-1780. The carving relates to the mask carved console table in the Karolik Collection. Exhibited in the "Furniture of Eighteenth Century Boston," Museum of Fine Arts, Boston 1972, #10 in the catalogue.

Ht. 29″ Wd. 32½″ Dp. 15″

P2816 Classical mahogany dropleaf breakfast table, the turned column is supported on a platformed base finely carved on all four sides, top surface and ringed collar, supported on four outsplayed legs with acanthus carved panels ending in superb brass casters with the American eagle holding a cluster of arrows in bold relief, attributed to Henry Connelly, Philadelphia circa 1810-1820.

Ht. 29½″ Wd. (closed) 22½″ Lg. 45″
(open) 52½″

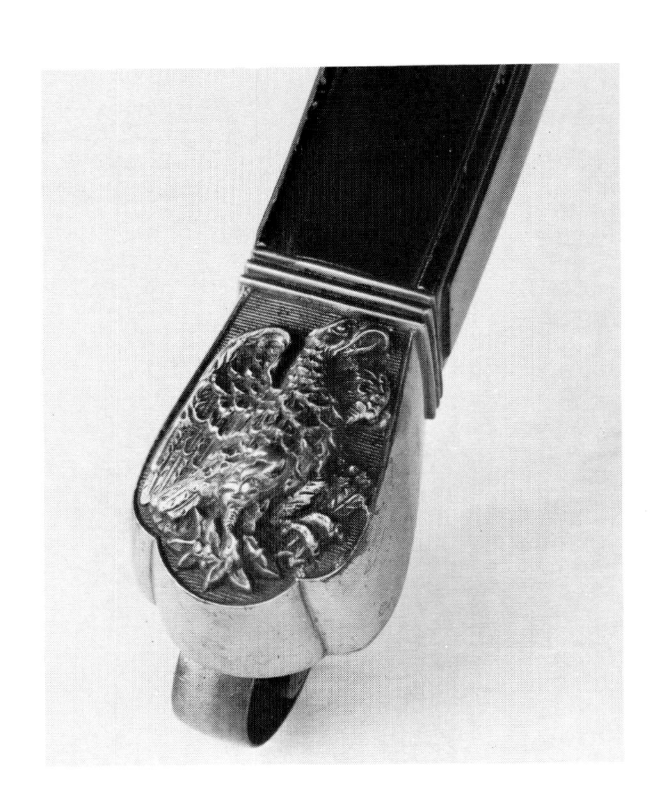

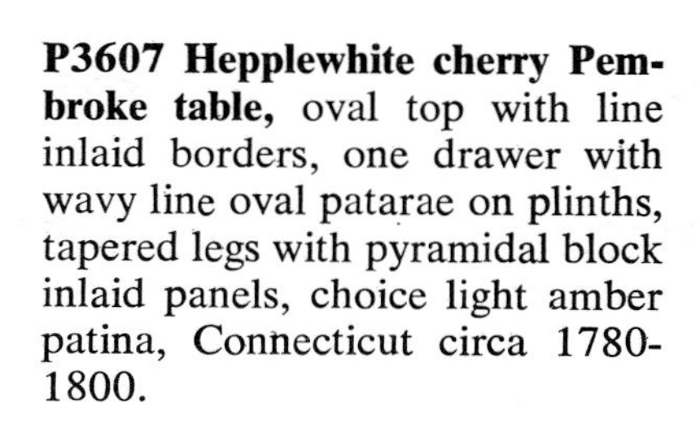

P3607 Hepplewhite cherry Pembroke table, oval top with line inlaid borders, one drawer with wavy line oval patarae on plinths, tapered legs with pyramidal block inlaid panels, choice light amber patina, Connecticut circa 1780-1800.

Ht. 28¾″ Wd. 19½″ (closed)
42″ (open)
Lg. 30″

P3652 Hepplewhite mahogany dressing table, arched center with two large satinwood fan inlaid spandrels, flanked by two square drawers with inlaid circular borders, one long drawer above, original chased ring brasses with urn center, tapered legs with etched bellflower inlay, flat shaped shelf below with line inlaid borders, choice color tulip-poplar secondary, Newport, Rhode Island, circa 1780-1800.

Descended in the family of Captain Joseph Allen, Revolutionary War Sea Captain of Newport, Rhode Island. The oil portrait of Captain Joseph Allen is on view in the Newport Historical Society.

Ht. 31¾″ Wd. 35″ Dp. 19¾″

P3606 Hepplewhite mahogany oval top pembroke table, the tapered legs inlaid on two sides with rare five petalled bellflower drops, the effect is created by interposing one bellflower within another, stiles with rectangular panels with quadrant corners, choice craftsmanship and color, Baltimore, Maryland, circa 1780-1800. A pembroke table with this distinctive inlay is illustrated in "Baltimore Furniture" catalogue #21.

Ht. 29″ Lg. 36″ Wd. 20¼″ closed
44¼″ open

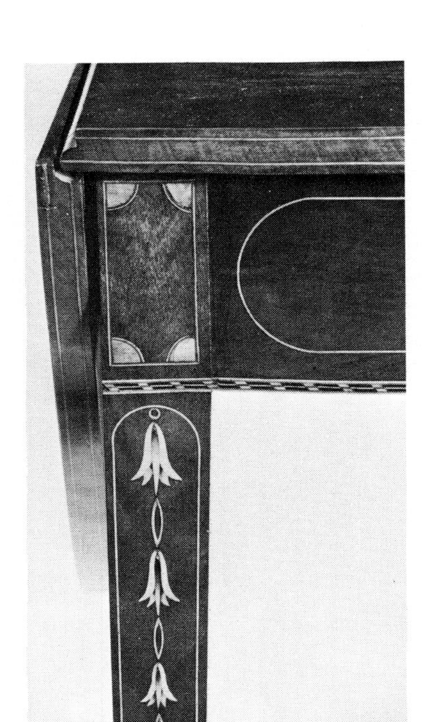

P3611 Hepplewhite mahogany one drawer inlaid end table, the top inlaid with dark and light quadrants and diamond center panel, tapered line inlaid legs with light wood panels on plinths and oval paterae below, fine medium brown color, Springfield or Athol, Massachusetts, circa 1780-1800. The table is deeper than it is wide, making it particularly useful as an end table or bedside table.

Ht. 28¾″ Wd. 17¾″ Dp. 21⅜″

P3562 Silver tankard, tapering sides with applied band, stepped and high domed cover, bell shaped finial, scrolled thumbpiece, moulded hinge plate with oval drop, scrolled handle with oval dish terminal, the front bears the contemporary engraved coat of arms of the Porter family of Boston, marked JOHN BURT, made by John Burt, Boston, Massachusetts, circa 1735-1745. A closely similar tankard by John Burt is illustrated "American Silver in the Yale University Art Gallery" Buhler & Hood, plate 114.

Ht. 7″ Dia. (base) 4½″

P3659 Queen Anne walnut lowboy of rare small size, center drawer fan carved with thumbnail border, choice mellow light brown patina, Massachusetts circa 1740-1760.

This lowboy was sold by us in 1936 and recently re-purchased.

Ht. 30½″ Wd. 31¼″
Dp. 19¼″

P3664 Pair of Sheraton mahogany serving tables, each with one row of divided drawers and one long drawer with original lion ring brasses, flanked by turret reeded columns, below are shelves with concave fronts, bulbous reeded and turned legs, conforming shaped tops with reeded borders, fine bronze patina, New York circa 1800-1810. The tables have slight variation in detail but come from the same source. A similar example is illustrated Cornelius "Masterpieces of Duncan Phyfe" plate XLIX.

Ht. 36″ Wd. 36½″ Dp. 20¾″

Ht. 36½″ Wd. 36½″ Dp. 20¾″

National Treasures

Americans have only recently awakened to the realization that they have a great artistic heritage. Older countries have long revered their national treasures and correspondingly held respected authorities on their cultural masterpieces in high esteem. As the great art of a country becomes a vital part of a nation's pride and contributions, those few who are best qualified to interpret and evaluate it assume a vital and recognized role in separating masterpieces from the nearly great, the genuine from the fraudulent, and the creations that most brilliantly express the unique character of its people.

A lifetime of experience and study is necessary to qualify as an art expert whether so honored by one's native land or not. The subtlety of connoisseurship and the delicate nuance of true expertise in American furniture is achieved by a synthesis of a knowledge of structure, wood, cabinetmaking techniques, oxidation of woods, stylistic features and the techniques of restoration. The sum total of these factors however is not enough.

There is a plus element—undefinable—that weaves its thread throughout to add that final touch probably for lack of better definition known as "art" or "the art."

We hope that the recognition of what we have to offer in this respect will be utilized to the fullest by those interested in either the academic study of Americana or in the furtherance of the status of their own collections.

We believe there are a number of pieces in this brochure which qualify as national treasures and cannot be exceeded in either beauty or value with any comparable form that is or has been offered for sale.

HAROLD SACK   ALBERT M. SACK   ROBERT M. SACK

P3696 Queen Anne maple side chair, violin splat, yoke crest, trumpet legs with disc pad feet, old black paint, New York circa 1730-1740.

Ht. 41″

P3743 William and Mary banister back armchair, moulded banisters, yoke shaped crest, arrow turned back posts with ogival moulded terminals, serpentine arms, turned legs with trumpet ball feet intact, sausage turned frontal stretchers, old black paint, the contemporary brand A VP on the back rail is that of an old New York Dutch family, New York circa 1710-1730.

Ht. 43¼″ Wd. 24″ (across arms)

P3695 Early maple slat back armchair, old black paint, graduated serpentine slats, fine bulbous turned frontal stretchers, Massachusetts circa 1710-1730.

Ht. 46½″ Wd. 23½″

P3758 Diminutive three masted ship model of exquisite detail, carved of wood with ivory fittings and ivory figurehead. 54 guns, mounted on galleried platform decorated with maritime etching, the gallery with green leaves, the case and floor with intricate straw inlaid patterns, circa 1790-1820.

Case Ht. 14¼″ Wd. 15½″ Dp. 6¾″

P3734 Painting of American ship bearing the American flag in a Chinese port with a view of a harbor and ships in background, Chinese early 19th century.

Ht. 22″ Wd. 27½″

P3688 Transitional Queen Anne birch rush seat corner chair, turned legs, the front leg ending in a pad foot, ball and ring turned stretchers, vase shaped pierced splats, shaped yoke, North Shore, Massachusetts, circa 1750-1770.

Ht. 31¼″ Wd. 28½″

P3733 Queen Anne walnut armchair, cabriole legs ending in drake feet, beautifully modelled serpentine arms with scooped arm rests and scrolled knuckle arm terminals, vase shaped splat, serpentine crest rail, mellow light brown patina, Philadelphia circa 1750-1760.

While Philadelphia side chairs of this transitional form are numerous, few armchairs ever appear on the market.

Ht. 39¾″ Wd. 27½″

P3747 Queen Anne walnut side chair, balloon seat, cushioned pad feet, block and arrow turned stretchers, violin splat, yoke shaped crest rail, fine old color and crisp modelling, Massachusetts circa 1740-1760.

A family label inside the frame reads: Mary Fisk was married to Rev. John Noyes 1758.

Ht. 40″

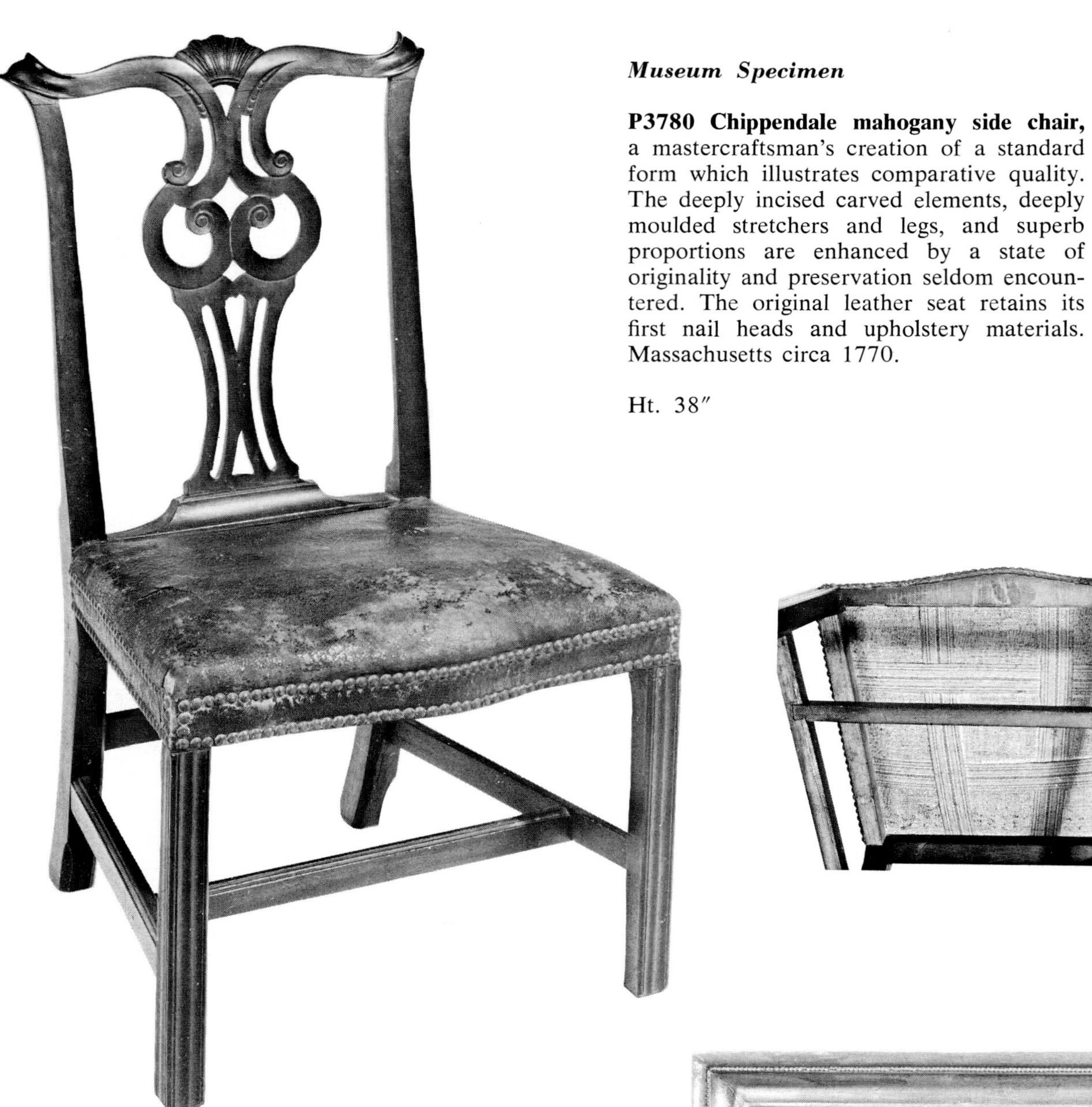

Museum Specimen

P3780 Chippendale mahogany side chair, a mastercraftsman's creation of a standard form which illustrates comparative quality. The deeply incised carved elements, deeply moulded stretchers and legs, and superb proportions are enhanced by a state of originality and preservation seldom encountered. The original leather seat retains its first nail heads and upholstery materials. Massachusetts circa 1770.

Ht. 38″

P3739 Portrait of Mathilda Margaret Temple of Boston depicting a young girl in olive green dress wearing brown beads, in original gilt frame bearing a family inscription on back, American early 19th century.

Ht. 23½″ Wd. 19½″

P1014 Chippendale mahogany side chair and companion slipper chair, interlaced splats with diamond centers, cabriole legs with pointed knees, claw and ball feet with swept back talons, turned stretchers with block and ring turned medial stretchers, Massachusetts circa 1760-1780.

This rare combination was sold by us ten years ago and recently repurchased.

Ht. (side chair) 37″ Ht. (slipper chair) 34″

P3729 Chippendale mahogany upholstered stool, square legs with beaded edges, stretchers with moulded top surface, original scrolled corner brackets, curly maple seat frame, Massachusetts circa 1760-1780.

Pre-Revolutionary stools of incontrovertible American origin are of the greatest rarity.

Ht. 17½″ Wd. 24½″ Dp. 16¼″

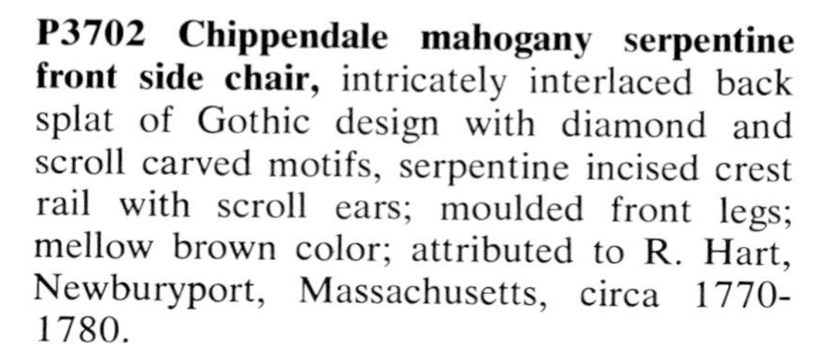

P3702 Chippendale mahogany serpentine front side chair, intricately interlaced back splat of Gothic design with diamond and scroll carved motifs, serpentine incised crest rail with scroll ears; moulded front legs; mellow brown color; attributed to R. Hart, Newburyport, Massachusetts, circa 1770-1780.

Ht. 38″

P3759 Mahogany serpentine front tea caddy, choice crotch veneered case, diamond inlaid escutcheon; the interior is in three circular compartments, the center compartment with the original creamware tea caddy, Massachusetts circa 1780-1790. This tea caddy comes from the Green Homestead in Windsor, Vermont, and descended from Isaac Green who married Ann Barrett in 1792.

Ht. 7¾″ Wd. 13″ Dp. 7″

P3760 Chippendale San Domingan mahogany corner chair with stop fluted front leg, interlaced pierced "pretzel" splat, fine old finish, school of John Townsend, Newport, Rhode Island, circa 1760-1780.

Ht. 32⅛″ Wd. 29½″

P3713 Pair of Sheraton mahogany side chairs, beautiful drapery carved splats with pyramidal moulded and carved column framed by scrolls, arched crest with raised carved panel, tapered moulded legs, stretchers, fine bronze patina, attributed to John Aitken, Philadelphia, circa 1795-1810.

A chair (or chairs) with identical backs but with inlaid legs in Mount Vernon were made for George Washington by John Aitken.

Ht. 36¾″

P3703 Hepplewhite mahogany shield back side chair, ribbon and bellflower carved back, tapered line inlaid legs, spade feet, New York circa 1780-1800.

Ht. 37½″

P235 Pair of Hepplewhite mahogany slipper armchairs, oval backs with drapery, floral and rosette carved backs, incurvate arms with moulded fronts continuing to beautiful incurvate arm supports, tapered moulded legs, the chairs retain the original huge hard pine vertical corner blocks and seat frames, Maryland circa 1780-1800.

Ht. 35½″ Wd. 22″

P3714 Pair of Hepplewhite mahogany side chairs, moulded shield backs with vertical emphasis, pointed base with carved crescents from which radiate drapery and acanthus carved splats with bellflower carved centers, tapered legs ending in spade feet, the seat frames have dovetailed braces running from front to rear, New York circa 1780-1800.

Ht. 39¼″

P3683 Hepplewhite mahogany wing chair, serpentine wings and crest, tapered moulded legs, stretchers, original finish, Massachusetts circa 1770-1790.

Ht. 48¼″ Wd. 35″ Dp. 28½″

P3701 Miniature Sheraton mahogany four post bed, bulbous turned head and foot posts, shaped headboard, New England circa 1800-1810. Either a scale model or doll's bed.

Ht. 17¾″ Wd. 10¼″ Lg. 18″

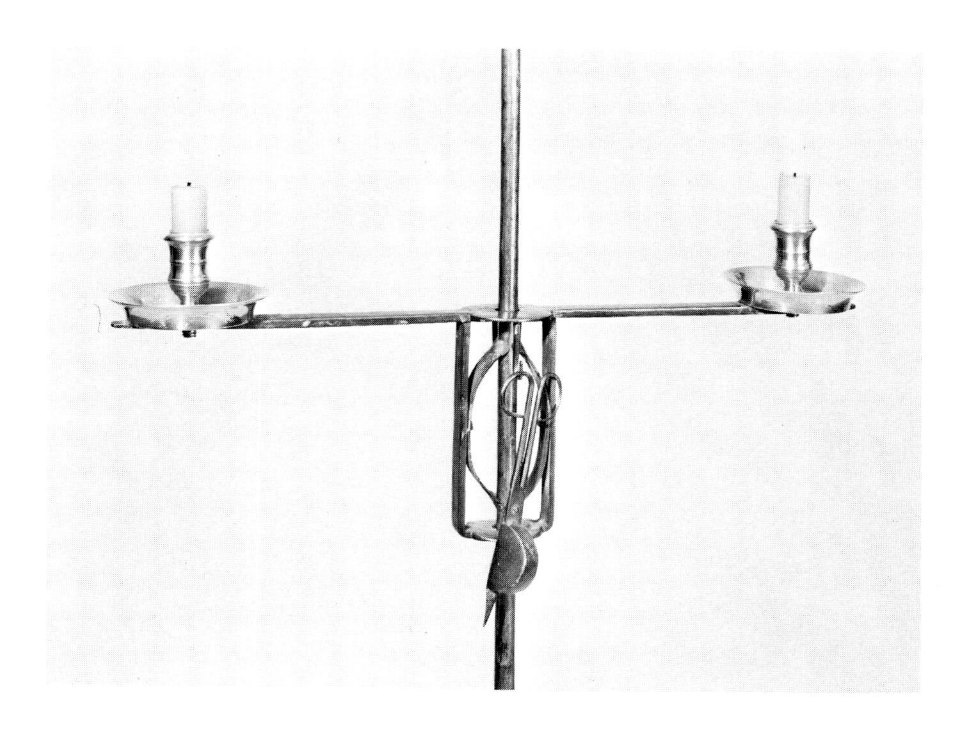

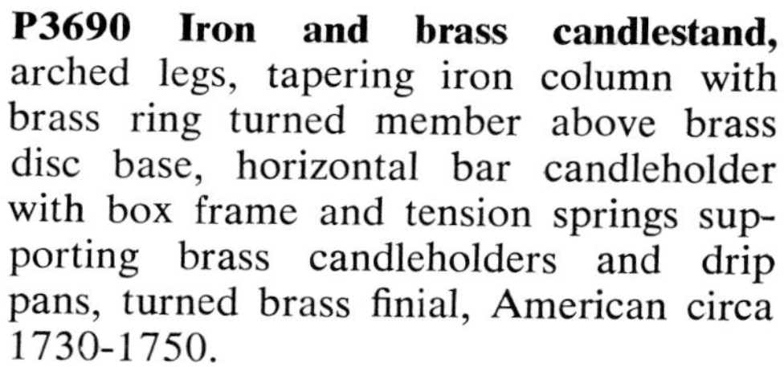

P3690 Iron and brass candlestand, arched legs, tapering iron column with brass ring turned member above brass disc base, horizontal bar candleholder with box frame and tension springs supporting brass candleholders and drip pans, turned brass finial, American circa 1730-1750.

The iron and brass candlestand is considered a collector's prize and rarely does an authentic example appear on the market. This finely wrought standard is original in all particulars including the candleholders, drip pans and finial.

Ht. 69″

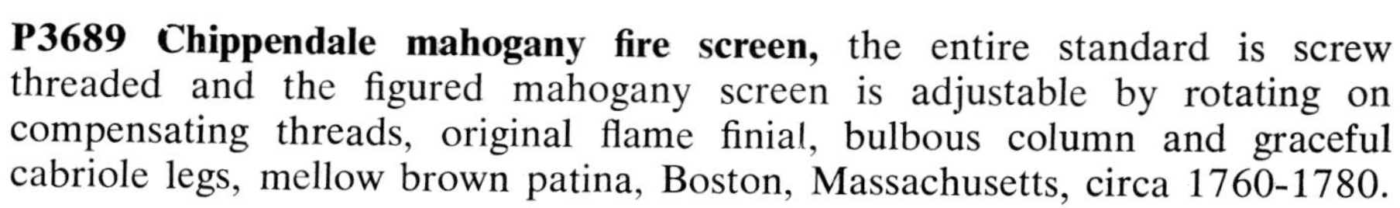

P3689 Chippendale mahogany fire screen, the entire standard is screw threaded and the figured mahogany screen is adjustable by rotating on compensating threads, original flame finial, bulbous column and graceful cabriole legs, mellow brown patina, Boston, Massachusetts, circa 1760-1780.

A fire screen of this form with a needlework panel embroidered by the daughters of Dr. Johnson, first president of Columbia University is illustrated in "Furniture of the Olden Time" by Frances Clara Morse, plate 328. It has the same threaded column and flame finial.

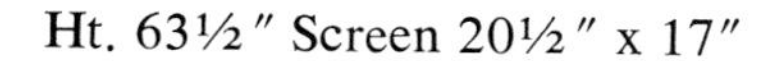

Ht. 63½″ Screen 20½″ x 17″

P3799 Chippendale cherry block front bureau, bold convex blocked drawers, ogee bracket feet, cyma curved moulded top, fine amber color, Connecticut circa 1760-1780.

Descended in the Pratt family.

P3735 Portrait of a child in lavendar dress, holding wicker basket in her left hand, right hand resting on table with fruit, oval background, American circa 1830-1850.

Ht. 33¼″ Wd. 26¼″

P3732 Chippendale mahogany mirror with scrolled crest and base, carved and gilded phoenix silhouetted in crest, beautiful light golden patina, probably Massachusetts, circa 1760-1780.

Ht. 30¾″ Wd. 19″

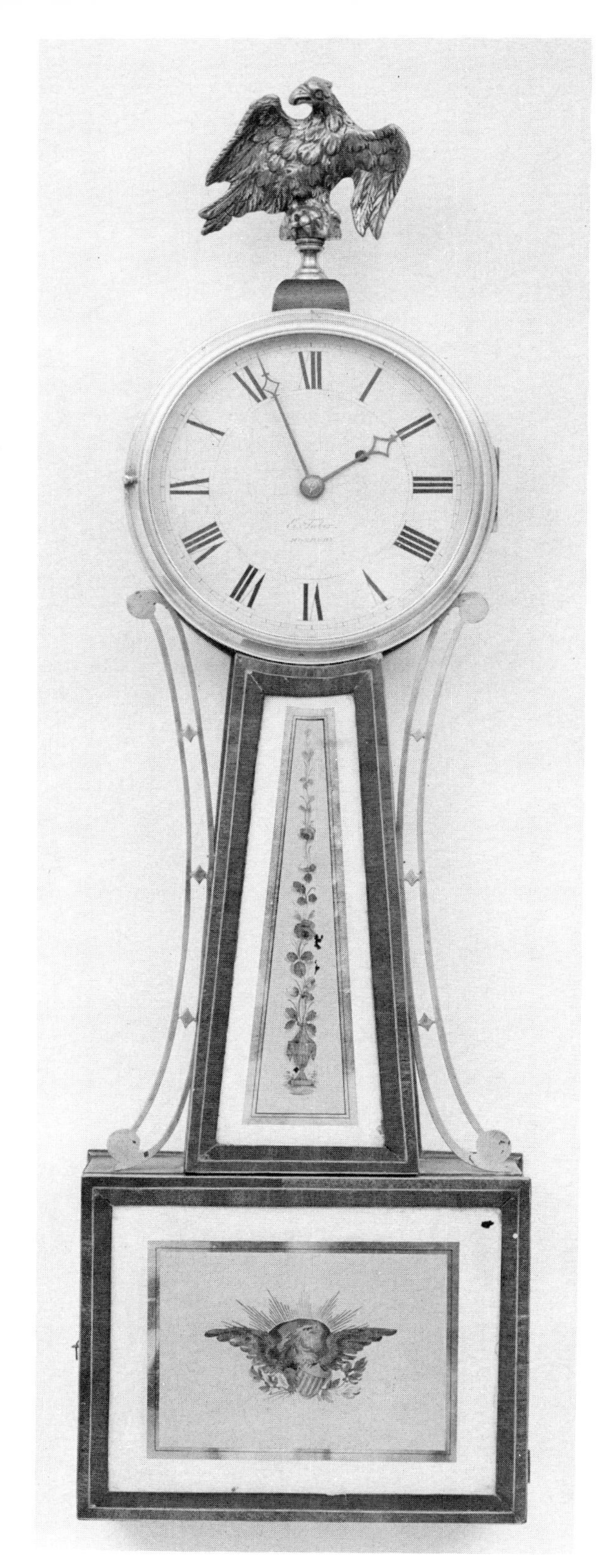

P3752 Banjo clock with original eglomise glass panels, the door panel depicting the American eagle and shield in gilt with ochre background, the waist panel with urn and flowers, inlaid and crossbanded borders, original brass eagle finial, dial inscribed "E. Taber, Roxbury, made by Elnathan Taber, Roxbury, Massachusetts, circa 1810-1820.

Ht. 33½″ Wd. 9¾″ Dp. 3⅝″

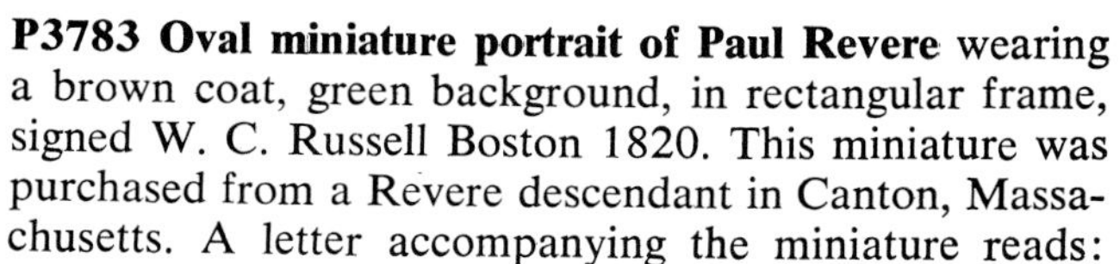

P3783 Oval miniature portrait of Paul Revere wearing a brown coat, green background, in rectangular frame, signed W. C. Russell Boston 1820. This miniature was purchased from a Revere descendant in Canton, Massachusetts. A letter accompanying the miniature reads:

"The miniature painting of Paul Revere to the best of my knowledge has always been in my family. It was given to me by my grandmother, Susan Revere Chapin, a great grand-daughter of Paul Revere, since I was named for her.

Susan Revere Edgerley"

Portrait measurement 7⅞″ x 2⅛″

P3742 Hepplewhite mahogany inlaid mantle clock with concave dish dial inscribed D. Wood; the upper case door with circular opening is inlaid with striated oval spandrels, wavy crest with inlaid central plinth; the lower case fronted by door with similar striated oval panels and dotted inlaid borders, ogee bracket feet, mellow light brown patina, made by David Wood, Newburyport, Massachusetts, circa 1800-1810.

Ht. 32″ Wd. 11¾″ Dp. 6″

P3716 Sheraton marble and gilt Bilboa mirror of exceptional quality and beauty; the festooned crest is centered by an oval panel in beaded border with painted landscape scene with seated figure, Spanish for the American market circa 1790-1800. This mirror descended in the Nell Stoddard family of Plymouth, Massachusetts.

Ht. 33″ Wd. 15″

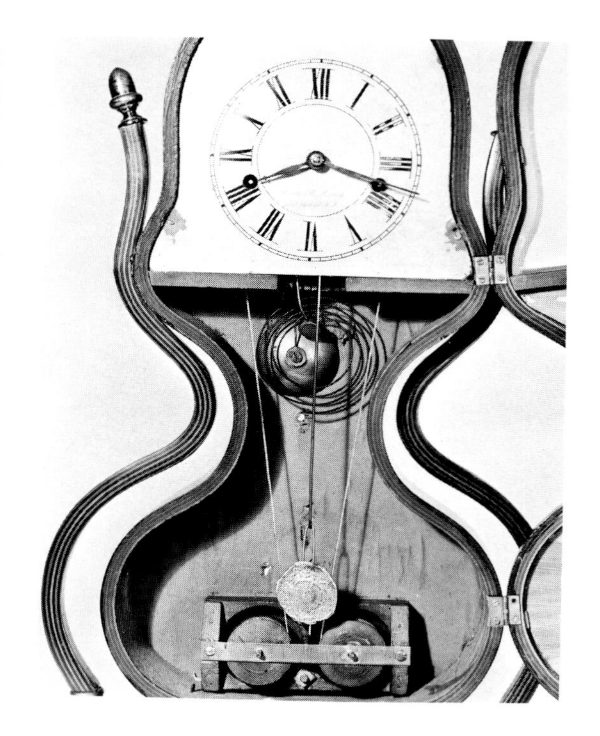

P3754 Acorn clock with original eglomise glass panel and fusee movement, the case borders and brackets are formed of laminated dark and light strips, the brackets terminate in brass acorns, dial inscribed "Forestville Manuf. Bristol, Ct. USA", Bristol, Connecticut, circa 1840-1850. An acorn clock by this maker and scene is in the Metropolitan Museum.

Ht. 24¼″ Wd. 14½″

P3721 Sheraton gilt "tabernacle" mirror with eglomise glass panel depicting the Naval engagement of the Constitution and Guerriere in cartouche border with green background, original gilt and glass, Boston, Massachusetts, circa 1800-1815.

This historic Naval battle is depicted by an artist of superior ability.

Ht. 30½″ Wd. 13¾″

P3756 Queen Anne walnut small desk on frame, the frame with graceful cyma curved scrolled apron, squared legs tapering to slender ankles and platformed pad feet, one drawer in frame and two drawers in desk section with the original engraved brasses, the desk interior contains a sliding well, beautiful brown patina of great depth and mellowness, Massachusetts circa 1730-1750.

Ht. 38¾″ Wd. 26¼″ Dp. 16¾″
Wr. Ht. 30¼″

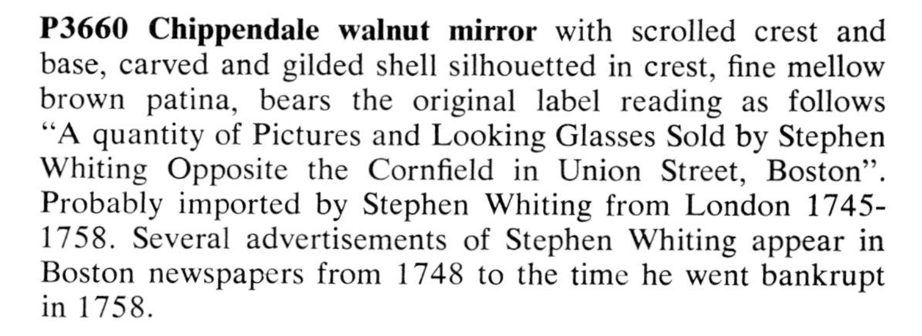

P3660 Chippendale walnut mirror with scrolled crest and base, carved and gilded shell silhouetted in crest, fine mellow brown patina, bears the original label reading as follows "A quantity of Pictures and Looking Glasses Sold by Stephen Whiting Opposite the Cornfield in Union Street, Boston". Probably imported by Stephen Whiting from London 1745-1758. Several advertisements of Stephen Whiting appear in Boston newspapers from 1748 to the time he went bankrupt in 1758.

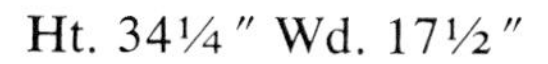

Ht. 34¼″ Wd. 17½″

P3722 Matched pair of Chippendale mahogany mirrors with scrolled crests and bases, phoenix birds facing each other silhouetted in crest, undoubtedly made in the same shop, probably Massachusetts circa 1760-1780.

Ht. 40¼″ Wd. 22½″

P3762 Chippendale walnut claw and ball foot lowboy, cabriole legs with webbed shell carved knees and graceful cyma curved knee brackets flowing into marginal scroll carved apron with webbed shell center, fluted quarter columns, cyma curved moulded top with retaining mouldings below, original brasses and fine mellow light brown patina, Philadelphia circa 1760-1780.

Ht. 30¼″ Wd. 33″ Dp. 20″

P941 Chippendale slant top desk of mottled mahogany grain and rare form, the case is formed with three blocked serpentine drawers, the end blocking concave, original brasses, supported on cabriole legs with superbly carved knees and ball and claw feet with hairy swept back talons, cartouche carved center pendant, attributed to John Cogswell, Boston, Massachusets, circa 1770-1790.

Comparison of the leg carving and hairy talons with those on the signed Cogswell chest-on-chest support the attribution.

Ht. 43¾″ Wd. 41″ Dp. 22½″
Wrg. Lvl. 33″

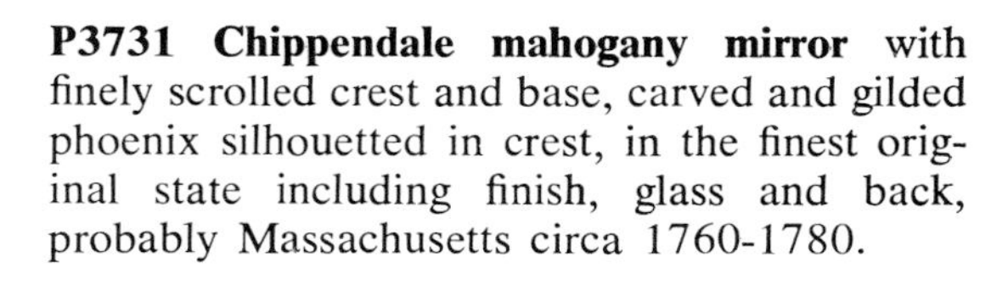

P3731 Chippendale mahogany mirror with finely scrolled crest and base, carved and gilded phoenix silhouetted in crest, in the finest original state including finish, glass and back, probably Massachusetts circa 1760-1780.

Ht. 34¼″ Wd. 19¼″

P3692 Chippendale cherry highboy, squared cabriole legs removeable in the Newport manner, claw and ball feet, the balls highlighted with black paint, graceful cyma curved scrolled apron, the upper case with free standing spiral columns frame five graduated long drawers and upper row of three divided drawers with small fan carved center drawer, original brasses, fine amber patina, Norwich, Connecticut, circa 1760-1785. This piece came to Monterey, California, in the nineteenth century. It is illustrated in the California issue of ANTIQUES, January 1954, page 55.

Ht. 75″ Wd. 39″ Dp. 19″

P3766 Chippendale walnut mirror of tall slender proportion, scrolled crest and base, carved and gilded shell silhouetted in crest, carved and gilded mirror border, fine patina, American or English circa 1750-1780.

Ht. 48½″ Wd. 23″

P3681 & 3682 Sheraton decorated three chair back settee and four side chairs, balloon rush seats, outsplayed turned legs, decorated with musical motifs on crest, New York circa 1800-1810.

Formerly in the Music Room, Van Schuyler Mansion in Albany.

Settee
Ht. 32½″ Wd. 74″ Dp. 25½″

Chairs
Ht. 32″

P3724 Pair of armorial coats of arms, water colors in original black moulded frames. The arms are those of Sullivan and Lincoln, the Lincoln arms displaying the American flag, painted by John Coles, Charlestown, Massachusetts, circa 1800-1810. Coles was a portrait painter who studied under Gilbert Stuart.

A family history provides the following background. The Sullivan arms are those of James Sullivan (1744-1808). He was a delegate to the Continental Congress and the Committee of Safety. He founded and was first President of the Massachusetts Historical Society.

The Lincoln arms is for one branch of the family with which Abraham Lincoln was connected. His ancestors came from the branch that went to Hingham, Massachusetts. The Lincoln and Sullivan families were connected by marriage.

Ht. 15½″ Wd. 11½″

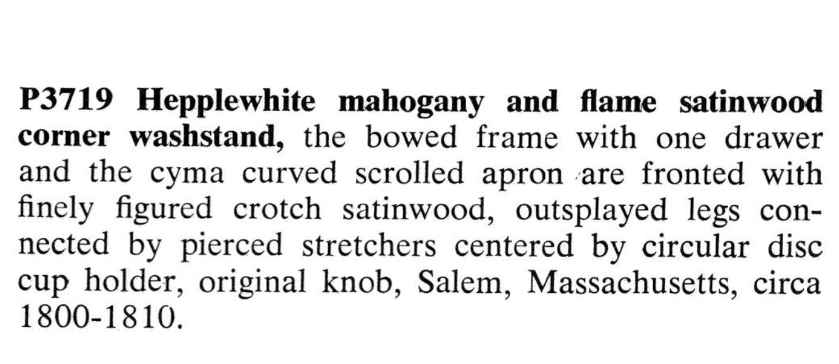

P3719 Hepplewhite mahogany and flame satinwood corner washstand, the bowed frame with one drawer and the cyma curved scrolled apron are fronted with finely figured crotch satinwood, outsplayed legs connected by pierced stretchers centered by circular disc cup holder, original knob, Salem, Massachusetts, circa 1800-1810.

A virtually identical example made by William Hook as a wedding present for his sister in 1808 in the Museum of Fine Arts, Boston, is illustrated Randall "American Furniture" plate 101.

Ht. 40½″ Wd. 23″ Dp. 16″

P960 Rare or unique Sheraton bow front mahogany and flame satinwood tambour desk, the base section is deeply bowed, the drawers fronted by beautifully figured flame satinwood and with original chased cyma curved brasses, ring turned feet, the top drawer opens to form the writing section; the tall upper section has bowed tambours centered by a long flame satinwood door and small drawers above, various patterns of inlaid borders complete the brilliant design, Salem, Massachusetts, or Portsmouth, New Hampshire, circa 1800-1810.

Ht. 5′ Wd. 44½″ Dp. 23″ W.L. 31½″

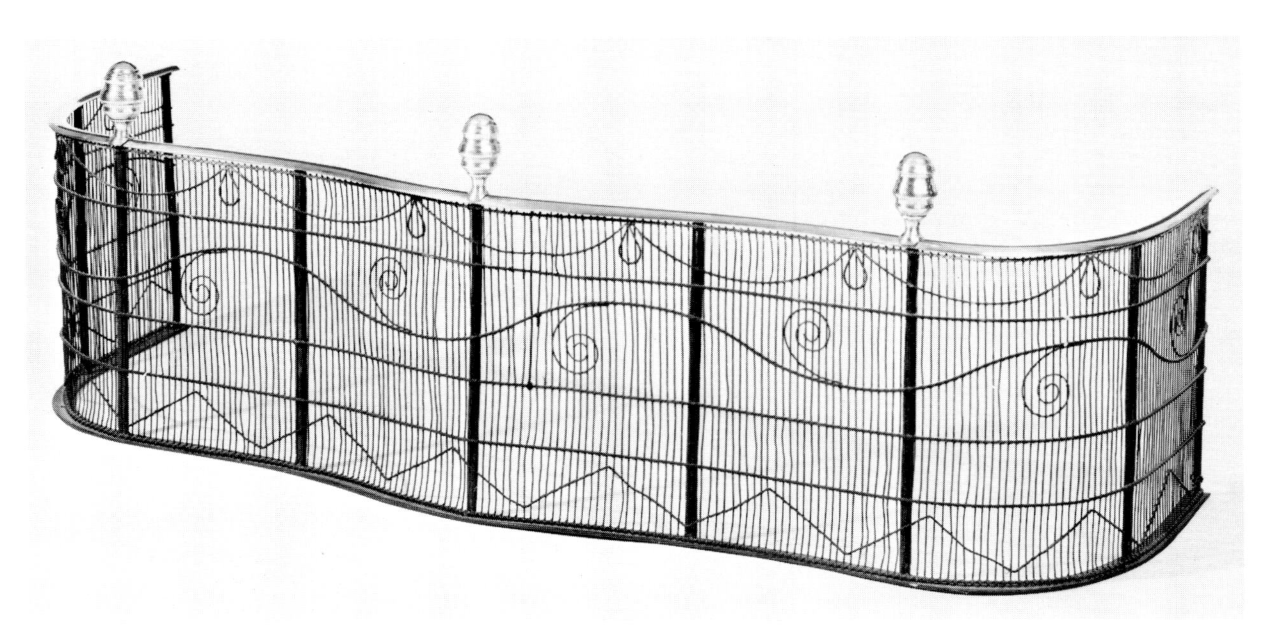

P3788 Wire and brass serpentine shaped fireplace fender with three turned brass finials, the vertical wires intersected by graceful scrolling, American circa 1800-1810.

Wd. 48¼″ Ht. 15½″ Dp. 15½″

P3717 Sheraton gilt "tabernacle" mirror, with eglomise glass panel depicting a series of American flags and cannon, leaf border, original gilt and back, Boston, Massachusetts, circa 1800-1815.

Ht. 24″ Wd. 11¼″

P3718 Sheraton gilt "tabernacle" mirror with eglomise glass panel depicting an American eagle and shield with ribboned border, original gilt and glass, Boston, Massachusetts, circa 1800-1815.

Ht. 26¾″ Wd. 12¼″

P3715 Sheraton gilt "tabernacle" mirror, eglomise glass panel depicting the three Graces in gilt with white background. A unique and outstanding feature of this mirror is the sanded gilt cylindrical columns. This sanded gilt technique is seen on frames that John Doggett fashioned for Gilbert Stuart portraits. Exceptional also is the brilliant state of the original gilt. Boston, Massachusetts, circa 1800-1810.

Ht. 35¼″ Wd. 19¼″

P3726 Chippendale San Domingan mahogany slant top desk, ogee bracket feet with straightish inner outline in the Newport manner, original bat wing brasses, blocked and shell carved interior, the shell of the center door with fluted base in scrolled border, scooped pigeonhole drawers of cyma curved outline, sliding well in fallboard, mellow brown patina, attributed to John Townsend, Newport, Rhode Island, circa 1760-1770. Comparison of the interior with our labelled John Townsend desk, Brochure 21, pages 6 and 7, supports the attribution. This desk was made for Isaac Sherman (1736-1817) of Newport. It was purchased by us from direct descendants. A family genealogy will be given to the purchaser.

Ht. 42¼″ Wd. 40½″ Dp. 23½″
Wr. Ht. 31″

P3800 Queen Anne birch lowboy with inlaid sunburst fan in concave blocked center drawer, the drawers front and side aprons and top are bordered by black and white inlay, a compass star inlay centers the top, original engraved brasses, light amber patina, Massachusetts or Connecticut circa 1730-1750.

Illustrated in Lockwood "Colonial Furniture in America," 1926, Vol. I, page 350, fig. XVI (supplement).

P3773 Chippendale brass andirons with vigorous claw and ball feet, square plinths, bulbous columns and ball terminals, conforming back stops, Rhode Island circa 1760-1780.

Ht. 20¾″ Dp. 21¾″

P508 Chippendale mahogany console table with original gray and white marble top contained in moulded frame with retaining moulding, veneered frame, beaded bordered apron, square fluted legs with pierced corner brackets, maple and white pine secondary, Massachusetts circa 1760-1780.

Ht. 33¼″ Wd. 54½″ Dp. 25½″

P3673 Chippendale walnut mirror with scrolled crest and base, carved and gilded cartouche silhouetted in crest, pressed gilded shell in base, carved and gilded mirror border, original glass, fine mellow patina, American or English circa 1750-1770.

Ht. 39½″ Wd. 23″

P3675 Chippendale walnut mirror with scrolled crest and base, carved and gilded cartouche silhouetted in crest, carved and gilded mirror border, fine mellow patina, American or English circa 1750-1770.

Ht. 39½″ Wd. 21½″

P3723 Hepplewhite mahogany secretary, lower case with four drawers with inlaid ivory diamond escutcheons, outsplayed French feet, upper case with two doors with Gothic arch mullions, ivory escutcheons, crossbanded panels which conceal drawers and pigeonholes, shaped crest with flame satinwood center panel and end plinths, original brass finials, choice mellow brown patina. This secretary is closely related to one made by Emery Moulton of Lynn, Massachusetts, suggesting an attribution to that maker. Massachusetts circa 1800-1810.

Ht. 6′ 5¼″ Wd. 39¼″ Dp. 21″

P3691 Hepplewhite cherry one drawer end table, delicate tapered line inlaid legs with inlaid cuffs, the drawer is tastefully inlaid with an oval in a rectangle, the top inlaid with diamond sunburst center panel and crossbanded borders, choice amber patina, Massachusetts, circa 1780-1800.

A stand of rare grace and refinement.

Ht. 27¾″ Wd. 18″ Dp. 17½″

P3677 Embroidered alphabetical sampler with poem, reading in oval "Nancy Prentis was born in the year of our Lord, 1790, August the 10, Finished Anno Domini 1800, Richmond, Virginia." Southern samplers of this early date are rare.

Ht. 22″ Wd. 23½″

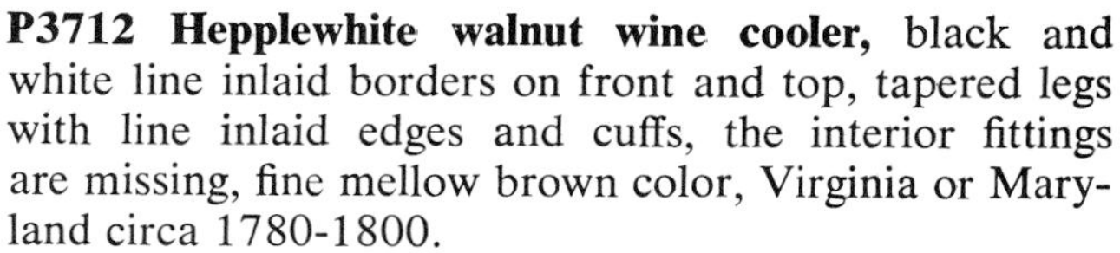

P3712 Hepplewhite walnut wine cooler, black and white line inlaid borders on front and top, tapered legs with line inlaid edges and cuffs, the interior fittings are missing, fine mellow brown color, Virginia or Maryland circa 1780-1800.

Ht. 29½″ Wd. 19⅛″ Dp. 19″

P3670 Courting mirror with eglomise glass floral decorated borders and center panel, in fine state, Continental for the American market, circa 1780-1800.

Ht. 15½″ Wd. 10½″

P3707 Sheraton mahogany sewing table, octagonal case and conforming reeded edged top, one drawer and sewing drawer, beautiful tapered reeded legs with horizontal ring turned turrets, superior craftsmanship and choice bronze patina, Boston, Massachusetts, circa 1800.

Ht. 28¼″ Wd. 21½″ Dp. 14½″

P3709 Sheraton mahogany sewing table, frame bowed on all four sides, one drawer and one sewing slide drawer, ring turned turret corners, bulbous reeded legs, fine mellow brown patina, Massachusetts circa 1800-1810.

Ht. 28¾″ Wd. 21⅛″ Dp. 17½″

P3662A Classical gilt convex mirror with beautifully sculptured eagle standing on urn and acanthus carved high plinth and holding chains of glass beads which drape to the candle holders, English circa 1800-1810.

Illustrated ANTIQUES December 1950 page 466.

Ht. 50½″ Wd. 25½″

PHILADELPHIA QUEEN ANNE ARMCHAIR

P3685 Queen Anne walnut armchair, solid spooned vase shaped splat with shaped panel bordered by four scrolled volutes, crest rail centered by shell bordered by scrolled volutes, incurvate scooped arms ending in bold knuckle terminals, incurvate arm supports, horseshoe seat, original seat frame, cabriole legs with shell carved knees and knee returns with scrolled volutes, stockinged feet, mellow brown original patina, Philadelphia circa 1740-1760.

Descended in the Brown family of Marmora Township, New Jersey. Formerly on exhibit in the Metropolitan Museum of Art.

Ht. 42″ Wd. (across arms) 31¾″

THE JOHN BROWN CORNER CHAIR

Attributed to John Goddard

Newport, Rhode Island, circa 1760-1765

P937 Chippendale corner chair fashioned of San Domingan mahogany, four cabriole legs ending in high taloned claw and ball feet, the frontal knee rounded to conform to the rounding of the seat frame, deeply serpentined horseshoe seat, three serpentine arm supports enclosing interlaced "pretzel" splats of deeply spooned profile, continuous arm with dished elbow rests and scrolled terminals; the chair retains the original brown leather slip seat covering with the contemporary name "Brown" on the maple seat frame; the deep brown finish is the original with great depth, the light sapwood is carefully chosen to highlight the knees in lieu of carving. The attribution to John Goddard seems assured since it is known that John Goddard was the favorite craftsman for the Brown brothers of Providence. This chair was one of a pair made for John Brown of Providence. It was given by him to his daughter Sarah Brown who married Karl Herreschoff of Bristol, Rhode Island. The chair was sold about ten years ago by Mrs. Sidney Herreschoff of Bristol and purchased by Israel Sack, Inc. It was sold to Lansdell K. Christie by Israel Sack, Inc. and repurchased from his estate. The mate to the chair, property of Norman Herreschoff, is on loan at the John Brown House, Providence.

Ht. 31½″ Wd. 28¾″

Exhibited "American Art from American Collections," Metropolitan Museum of Art, 1963, catalogue #57.

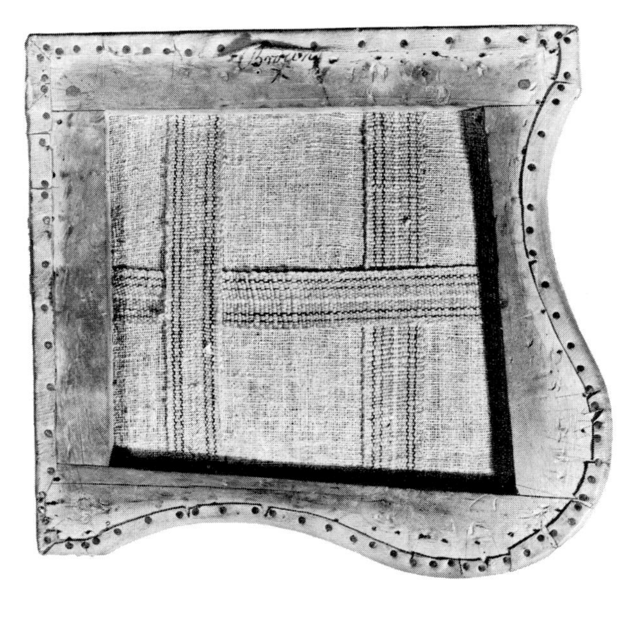

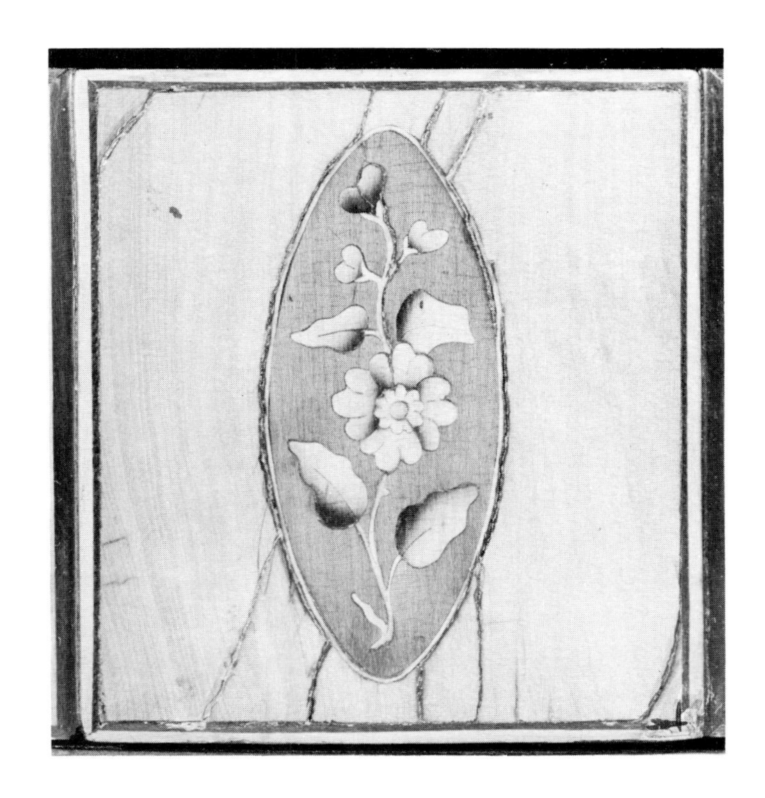

P3744 Hepplewhite mahogany D shaped sideboard, serpentine center long drawer with floral urn in satinwood panel flanked by two small drawers, recessed center cupboard compartment flanked by convex turrets and bottle drawers which retain the original blown glass decanters; the legs and stiles are fronted by satinwood panels with oval inlaid urns flanking the drawers, top bordered by spiral inlay, original octagonal brasses, superb mellow brown patina, New York circa 1780-1800. The grace and delicacy attained in a sideboard of this length shows the hand of a master designer. It is, to our knowledge, the only sideboard to retain its original decanters.

Ht. 41½″ Wd. 6′ 11½″ Dp. 28″

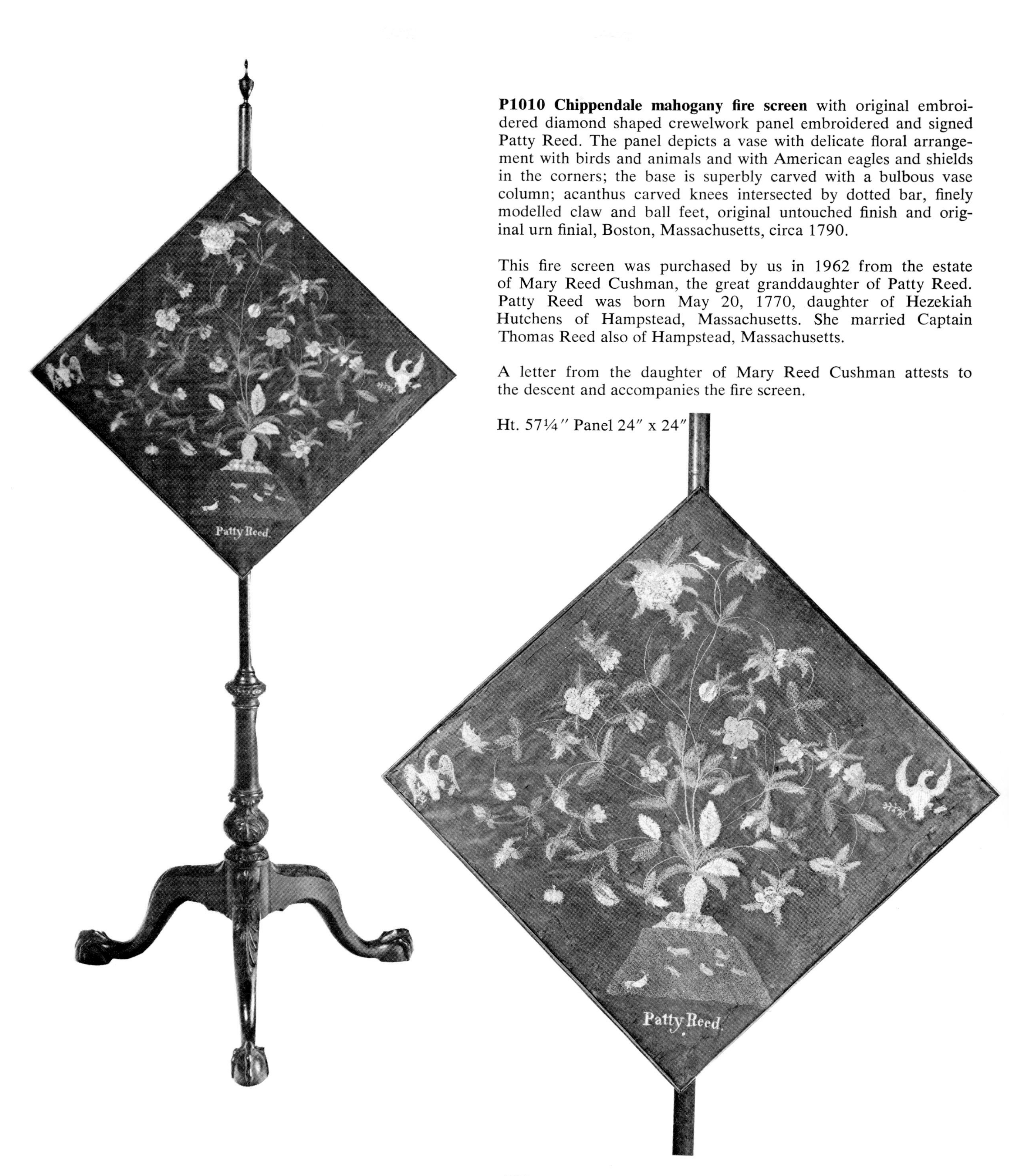

P1010 Chippendale mahogany fire screen with original embroidered diamond shaped crewelwork panel embroidered and signed Patty Reed. The panel depicts a vase with delicate floral arrangement with birds and animals and with American eagles and shields in the corners; the base is superbly carved with a bulbous vase column; acanthus carved knees intersected by dotted bar, finely modelled claw and ball feet, original untouched finish and original urn finial, Boston, Massachusetts, circa 1790.

This fire screen was purchased by us in 1962 from the estate of Mary Reed Cushman, the great granddaughter of Patty Reed. Patty Reed was born May 20, 1770, daughter of Hezekiah Hutchens of Hampstead, Massachusetts. She married Captain Thomas Reed also of Hampstead, Massachusetts.

A letter from the daughter of Mary Reed Cushman attests to the descent and accompanies the fire screen.

Ht. 57¼″ Panel 24″ x 24″

BLOCK AND SHELL SECRETARY DESK

Attributed to John Townsend

P3755 Chippendale secretary desk with block and shell carved doors, fashioned of "plum pudding" mahogany, the desk section with blocked and shell carved interior and scooped pigeonhole drawers closely related to the interior of our labelled John Townsend desk (brochure no. 21, pages 6 and 7) with a sliding well in the fallboard, original pine tree brasses and side carrying handles; the top drawer has two sliding wooden bolts, a feature seen on a labelled Townsend desk; ogee bracket feet; the upper section has two beautifully modelled block and shell carved doors flanked by deeply inset fluted quarter columns, the doors enclose an intricate fitted interior of vertical and horizontal partitions, closed bonnet top with bold inner mouldings and centered by a powerful fluted flame carved finial. The beauty of this superbly proportioned masterpiece is enhanced by a golden patina mellowing the drama of the plum pudding mottled figure. Attributed to John Townsend, Newport, Rhode Island, circa 1760-1770.

In seventy years of our career in American antiques, this is the first block and shell secretary we have had the privilege to own.

Ht. 8′2″ Wd. 40½″ Op. 23¾″ Wt. Level 30½″

P2466 Chippendale San Domingan mahogany bombe bureau, ogee bracket feet with finely scrolled inner outline, center pendant with double lobed base, the drawer fronts have mottled mahogany figure and the edges follow the outline of the bombe sides; the bureau is in mint original condition and features an exceptional original set of fire gilded chased brass handles and escutcheons of rococco design, Boston, Massachusetts, circa 1760-1780.

Ht. 31½″ Wd. 39″ Dp. 21½″

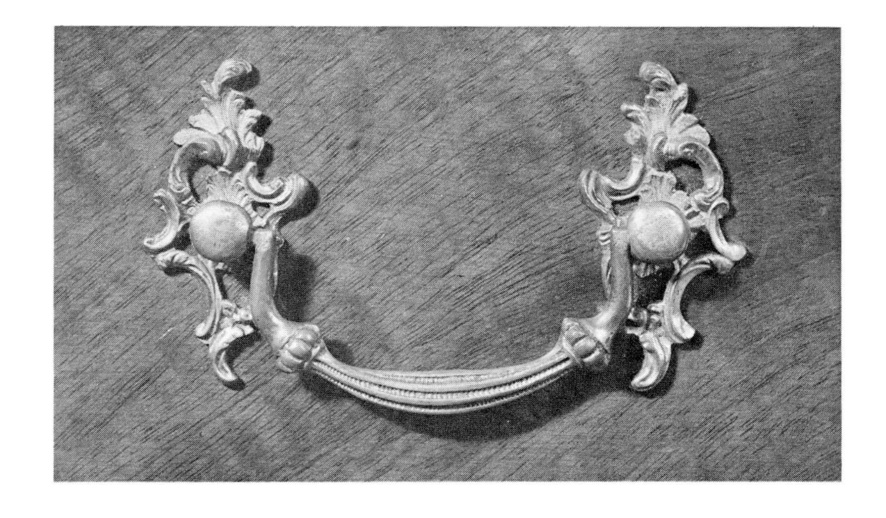

P3757 Queen Anne mahogany tea table with candle-slides, cabriole legs, with platformed wafer pad feet, beautifully scrolled cyma curved bulged apron, original concave tray mouldings with notched corners, Boston, Massachusetts, circa 1740-1760. The table is in the finest original state with the original finish, slide supports, and glue blocks intact.

This table descended in the Bradlee-Crowninshield family of Salem and was acquired by us from a descendant. Attached to the understructure is an old family label inscribed as follows:

"Very fine Queen Anne tea table—1720-1750; Belonged to Sarah (Bradlee) Fulton, sister in law of Robert Fulton, inventor of steamboat. She lived at the corner of Hollis and Tremont Sts. in Boston and her brothers were said to have dressed up as Indians in her house preparatory to participating in The Boston Tea Party."

Ht. 27″ Wd. 29″-43″ Dp. 19″

P3684 Chippendale mahogany wing chair with stop fluted legs, horizontal roll arms, serpentine wings and crest, stately vertical proportion, Goddard-Townsend group, Newport, Rhode Island, circa 1760-1780.

The chair is being exhibited with the original upholstery linen undercover and webbing. The legs and base retain the original finish.

Ht. 47″ Wd. 32¼″

P3753 Chippendale mahogany block and shell carved bureau with raised dished top, the finely modelled domed shells have broad fluted centers in scrolled borders, ogee bracket feet with marginal carved inner borders, Connecticut probably Middletown circa 1760-1780.

The piece is in untouched original condition including the finish and the beautiful chased bale brasses.

Ht. 36″ Wd. 38½″ Dp. 19″

P3740 Chippendale San Domingan mahogany block front bureau with sliding tray of rare small size and compact proportion, the vertical emphasis is accentuated by bold square blocking with equally bold original willow brasses, bracket feet with spurred and scrolled inner outline. The close grained dense mahogany has choice swirling figured grain. Massachusetts circa 1750-1770. Descended in the Storey Family of Boston.

Ht. 32⅛″ Wd. (top) 34½″ Dp. 21¼″

P3802 Set of eight Queen Anne walnut side chairs, balloon seats, cabriole legs ending in pad feet, block and arrow turned stretchers vase shaped splats, yoke shaped crest rails, nut brown color, Massachusetts circa 1740-1770.

This set was assembled a number of years ago by a collector. Some of the chairs came from Israel Sack, Inc. The chairs are well matched and show only slight variations.

P48 Chippendale mahogany blockfront chest-on-chest, the lower case with square blocking capped by rounded corners, bracket feet, the inner outline of which follows the line of the blocking, fan carved center pendant, the upper case with drawers flanked by fluted columns, the top row of drawers with fan carved center drawer and end drawers shaped to follow the line of the arch, bonnet top, original open flame carved finials with carved rims. This chest-on-chest is of rare narrow proportion accentuating the vertical emphasis. It retains the original brasses and a superb golden patina of great depth and mellowness. Attributed to Benjamin Frothingham, Charlestown, Massachusetts, circa 1760-1780.

Several characteristics of this piece are closely related to labelled Frothingham pieces and serve as the basis of the attribution: (1) the blocked bracket feet; (2) the shape of the blocking; (3) the open flame carved finials; (4) the shape of the arch; (5) the carved fan with thumbnail border. For illustrations of these labelled pieces see ANTIQUES Magazine, November 1952, pages 392 to 395 and Frontispiece.

Descended in the family of Benjamin Hall who married Hepzibah Jones in Medford, Massachusetts, in 1752.

Ht. 7′6″ Wd. 42½″

P3678 Pair of Queen Anne San Domingan mahogany dropleaf tea tables of diminutive size, square tops with cyma curved moulded edges, slender cabriole legs of beautiful serpentine outline ending in wafer pad feet, cyma curved aprons, bronze patina; Boston, Massachusetts, circa 1740-1760.

Both tables retain the original glue blocks. An unusual feature is the use of quarter round pine strips attached to the underside of the center boards to keep the leaves from sagging when down.

Authentic Queen Anne dropleaf tables thirty inches or under are considered collectors' prizes. To our knowledge a matched pair is unique.

Ht. 25¾″ Lg. 28½″ Wd. 28″

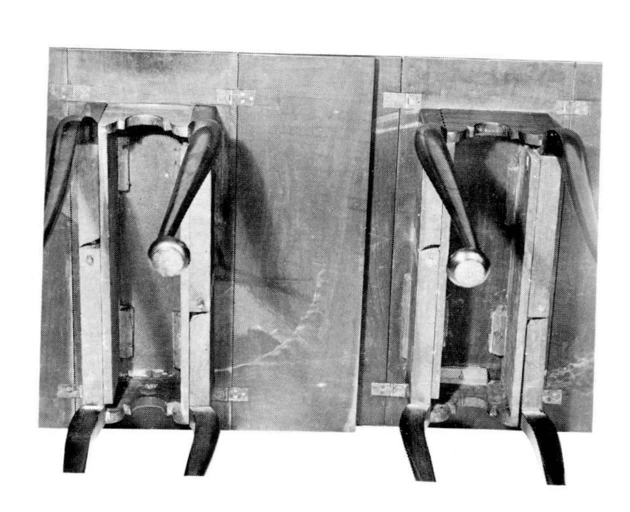

P3801 Chippendale mahogany ball and claw foot lowboy, deeply carved shell in center drawer with carved vines emanating from bold scrolls, bold scrolled volutes flank the shell centering the apron and are repeated on the knee returns, acanthus carved knees, chamfered fluted columns, moulded top with notched corners, Maryland circa 1760-1770.

The contemporary name "Shaw" is inscribed in the top drawer offering the interesting possibility of this being an early example of his work.

Ht. 31″ Wd. 33½″ Dp. 21½″

P3794 Chippendale mahogany serpentine front bureau with pointed ends, claw and ball feet, mellow light brown patina, Salem, Massachusetts, circa 1760-1780.

Ht. 33″ Wd. 38″ Dp. 21″

P3787 Hepplewhite mahogany tripod tilt top table, top with serpentine sides and pointed corners, slender urn shaped column, graceful serpentine legs, choice nut brown patina, Massachusetts circa 1770-1790.

Ht. 27½″ Top 21½″ x 21¼″

P3612 Classical tambour work table made entirely of satinwood, octagonal case with tambour reeded frontal shutter concealing two deep drawers, the canted corners, sides and back are faced with blind tambour reeding, the drawer and panels above are bordered by burl satinwood, the top lifts revealing an adjustable writing shelf and compartments; the case supported on four acanthus carved columns, platformed base with vertical fluting, acanthus carved legs ending in brass claw casters, superb golden patina of great warmth, attributed to Duncan Phyfe, New York circa 1810-1830.

Ht. 31″ Wd. 22¾″ Dp. 14½″

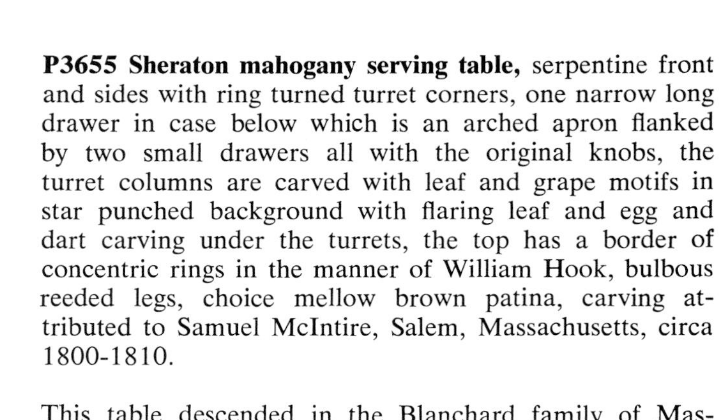

P3655 Sheraton mahogany serving table, serpentine front and sides with ring turned turret corners, one narrow long drawer in case below which is an arched apron flanked by two small drawers all with the original knobs, the turret columns are carved with leaf and grape motifs in star punched background with flaring leaf and egg and dart carving under the turrets, the top has a border of concentric rings in the manner of William Hook, bulbous reeded legs, choice mellow brown patina, carving attributed to Samuel McIntire, Salem, Massachusetts, circa 1800-1810.

This table descended in the Blanchard family of Massachusetts.

P3804 Hepplewhite mahogany secretary with inlay of American eagle, four drawers with inlaid borders in lower case section, outsplayed French feet, upper section with glass doors and diamond shaped mullions, shaped crest with center rectangular panel inlaid with eagle and shield with 18 stars in crescent, original brass finials, the center one a cast eagle on ball, choice mellow brown patina; Boston, Massachusetts, circa 1800-1815.

Ht. 6′ 5½″ Wd. 40″ Dp. 20″

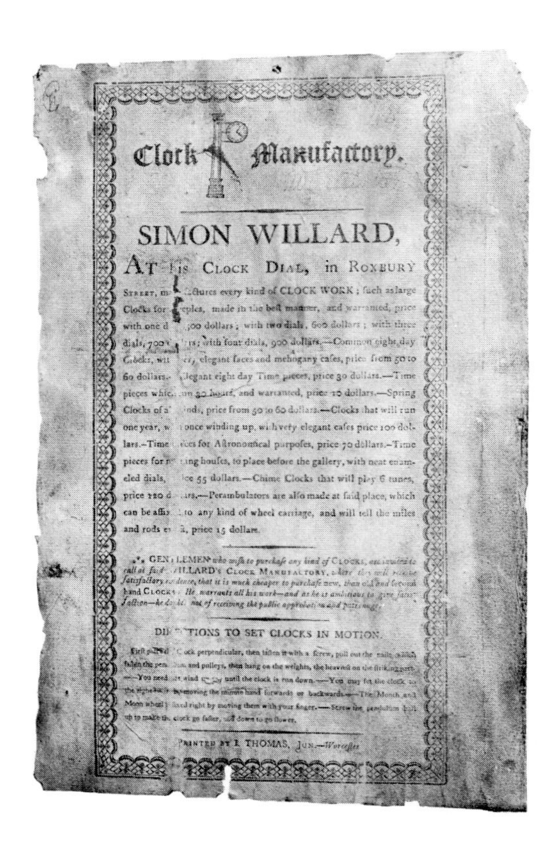

Clock Manufactory.

SIMON WILLARD,

AT [illegible]is CLOCK DIAL, in ROXBURY STREET, m[illegible]factures every kind of CLOCK WORK; fuch as large Clocks for [illegible]eeples, made in the beft manner, and warranted, price with one d[illegible] [illegible]00 dollars; with two dials, 600 dollars; with three dials, 700 [illegible]rs; with four dials, 900 dollars.—Common eight day Clocks, wit[illegible] [illegible], elegant faces and mahogany cafes, price from 50 to 60 dollars.—[illegible]legant eight day Time pieces, price 30 dollars.—Time pieces whic[illegible] [illegible]un 30 hours, and warranted, price 10 dollars.—Spring Clocks of a[illegible] [illegible]nds, price from 50 to 60 dollars.—Clocks that will run one year, w[illegible] once winding up, with very elegant cafes price 100 dollars.—Time [illegible]ces for Aftronomical purpofes, price 70 dollars.—Time pieces for m[illegible]ting houfes, to place before the gallery, with neat enameled dials, [illegible]ice 55 dollars.—Chime Clocks that will play 6 tunes, price 120 d[illegible]ars.—Perambulators are alfo made at faid place, which can be affix[illegible] to any kind of wheel carriage, and will tell the miles and rods e[illegible], price 15 dollars.

*** GEN[illegible]LEMEN *who wifh to purchafe any kind of* CLOCKS, *are invited to call at faid* [illegible]ILLARD'S CLOCK MANUFACTORY, *where they will receive fatisfactory [illegible]dence, that it is much cheaper to purchafe new, than old and fecond* hand CLOCKS. *He warrants all his work—and as he is ambitious to give fatisfaction—he doubt[illegible] not of receiving the public approbation and patronage.*

DIRECTIONS TO SET CLOCKS IN MOTION.

First put [illegible] Clock perpendicular, then faften it with a fcrew, pull out the nails which faften the pen[illegible] and pulleys, then hang on the weights, the heavieft on the ftriking part. —You need [illegible] wind [illegible] until the clock is run down.—You may fet the clock [illegible] [illegible] by moving the minute hand forwards or backwards.—The Month and Moon wheel [illegible] fixed right by moving them with your finger.—Screw the pendulum ball up to make th[illegible] clock go fafter, and down to go flower.

PRINTED BY I. THOMAS, JUN.—*Worcefter*

P3460 Hepplewhite mahogany tall clock of rare small size, the door and base are inlaid with fan quadrants, enamelled moon dial inscribed S. Willard, the clock retains the original label engraved by I. Thomas, Worcester, inside the door, made by Simon Willard, Roxbury, Massachusetts, circa 1796-1805. This clock was made for William Lord, ship Captain, of Kennebunkport, Maine. William Lord built the mansion shown in the daguerreotype which accompanies the clock. The clock stood in the Lord mansion until purchased by us from descendants.

Also accompanying the clock is a bill from Simon Willard and Son, February 1, 1858, for repairing and cleaning.

Ht. 7′ 6″

P3764 Sheraton gilt mirror, baluster columns with acanthus capitals, the crest is centered by a triangular eglomise glass panel in gilt and white in carved border supporting a superbly sculptured eagle holding drapery chains which connect to elliptical beaded urns with flaming torches standing on columns with ram's head terminals, American or English circa 1800-1810.

Ht. 49½″ Wd. 22¾″

P3790 Pair of Sheraton mahogany side chairs, the crests with sunburst carved panels, the back with reeded and fan carved slats, tapered reeded legs ending in spade feet, attributed to Slover and Taylor, New York, circa 1800-1810.

Ht. 34¾″

P3736 Primitive portrait of three children, the girl in center holding a shoe, the boy at left with arm resting on a plinth, the boy at right holding a cane, American circa 1830-1840.

Ht. 39″ Wd. 47″

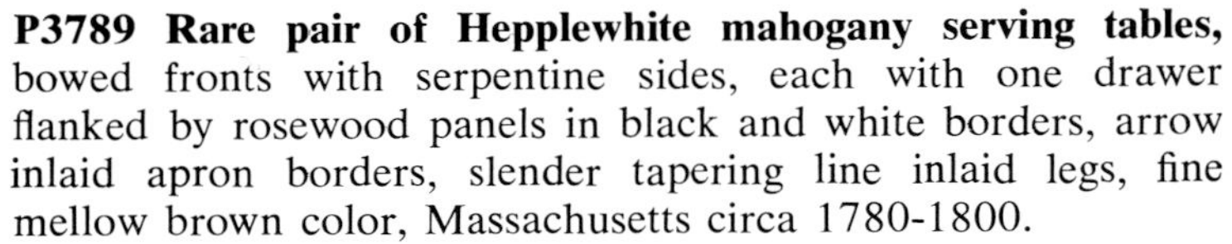

P3789 Rare pair of Hepplewhite mahogany serving tables, bowed fronts with serpentine sides, each with one drawer flanked by rosewood panels in black and white borders, arrow inlaid apron borders, slender tapering line inlaid legs, fine mellow brown color, Massachusetts circa 1780-1800.

Ht. 36″ Wd. 36″ Dp. 17¾″

P3705 Chippendale mahogany dropleaf table, circular top with rounded edge, finely modelled cabriole legs with original C-scrolled knee returns, superb sculptured claw and ball feet, cyma curved apron, original mellow brown patina, Boston, Massachusetts, or Newport, Rhode Island, circa 1760-1780.

The frame bears a family plaque engraved "Elizabeth Wanton 1712."

Ht. 27¼″ Lg. 24½″ Wd.

P3727 Chippendale mahogany tripod dishtop tea table with birdcage support, acanthus carved legs ending in finely sculptured claw and ball feet, eliptical ball turned column with gadrooned carving and slender tapering shaft, Philadelphia circa 1760-1780.

The carving and stance of this table rivals that on the great piecrust tea tables for which Philadelphia is famous. Few dishtop examples of this development are known.
Purchased by us from descendants of Governor John Willis Ellis of Rowan County, Virginia.

Ht. 28″ Dia. 33¾″

P3785 Chippendale walnut dish top tripod candlestand with birdcage support, one piece top with beautiful figured grain and warm ruddy patina, ball and ring turned column, graceful finely modelled cabriole legs, Philadelphia circa 1760-1780.

Descended in the Sharp-Leedom families of Philadelphia and purchased from direct descendants.

Ht. 28½″ Dia. 24½″

P3728 Sheraton mahogany sewing table, one drawer with original brass knobs with petalled chased backplates, thumbnail moulded edged top with rounded corners, finely turned bulbous reeded legs on brass casters, superb bronze patina, attributed to Thomas Seymour, Boston, Massachusetts, circa 1800-1815. The documented Thomas Seymour sewing table, "John and Thomas Seymour" plate 154 has related reeded legs, sewing slide on side, thumbnail bordered top and distinctive petalled chased knobs.

Ht. 29¾″ Wd. 21″ Dp. 15¾″

P3730 Courting mirror with painted glass borders and floral center panel in original pine case, rare small size and mint condition, European for the American market, circa 1780-1800.

Ht. 12½″ Wd. 7¾″

P3710 Sheraton mahogany and flame satinwood sewing table, rectangular case with turret corners and ring turned capitals with star punch motif, one drawer and sewing drawer, finely figured crotch satinwood veneer on all four sides, slender bulbous reeded legs with band of scribed rings, mellow light brown patina, Salem, Massachusetts, circa 1800.

Ht. 29½″ Wd. 20⅞″ Dp. 17¾″

P3779 Sheraton mahogany card table with serpentine front and sides and turret corners, the frame is veneered with panels of flame satinwood, oval center panel and apron bordered by interesting etched connecting diamond inlay, the edge and top border are crossbanded, the top crossbanding outlined by line inlay, both rear legs swing, bulbous reeded legs and bulbous feet, Massachusetts circa 1800-1810.

Ht. 29⅞″ Wd. 34″ Dp. 17″

P3720 Classical San Domingan mahogany dropleaf extension dining table, the beautifully figured mahogany top and leaves have a moulded edge and rounded corners; the leaves are supported by four ring turned columns each with brackets and outsplayed castered legs which pivot from a box frame, birch framework and brackets, Boston, Massachusetts, circa 1800-1815.

Ht. 27½″ Lg. 58″ Wd. 62½″ open—16¼″ closed

P3786 Chippendale carved and gilded overmantle mirror with the original three section bevelled glasses, the outer border with egg and dart carving with floral rosettes in the squared corners, the mirror border with astragal carving, English circa 1740-1760.

Wd. 43½″ Ht. 16″

P3778 Classical mahogany sofa, the back panel is finely carved and centered by a typical Salem basket with leaves and grapes in a star punch or snowflake background and bordered by spiral and acanthus carved borders; the spiral borders are repeated in the arms and seat terminating in delicately carved rosettes, outsplayed legs ending in acanthus brass casters, the brass mount under the basket is an effective touch; Attributed to Samuel Field McIntire, Salem, Massachusetts, circa 1810-1820.

Ht. 38″ Lg. 78″ Dp. 23½″

Non-Liquid Assets

Experience of close to three-quarters of a century in dealing in American antiques has taught us certain essentials.

Quality always pays off not only in terms of aesthetic satisfaction but also in terms of asset value.

Likewise experience has proven that the long term investment in genuine antiques of merit has been one of continuous success and has ridden out the cyclical recessions.

But a word of caution and admonition is in order. The long-term asset value is not to be confused with short-term liquidity or even long-term liquidity. Antiques should be purchased in the same vein as good real estate or land, and no one should count his collection as he does a stock portfolio which is convertible on a national basis into immediate cash, at least without the possibility of financial loss.

Our experience has also shown that many heirs have lived off the orderly sale of antiques as profitable assets. There is a distribution cost in the sale of any asset and antiques are no exception. A consistent growth in asset value is necessary to absorb this and of course the longer the span of time the more advantageous the expectancy of profit.

In the final analysis—the wise and proper selection of pieces of merit is the basic building block. The by-product is the financial investment.

HAROLD SACK   ALBERT M. SACK   ROBERT M. SACK

THE S S CHEST, NO. 81

Pilgrim oak "Hadley" chest with one drawer and bearing the initials SS for Sarah Smith, daughter of Deacon John Smith of Hadley, Massachusetts, made in Hadley, Massachusetts, circa 1700-1710. This piece is in the finest original state with a dark brown patina of great character. The bale handles are later additions.

This chest is illustrated in "The Hadley Chest" by Luther, page 112. The page from Luther's book tracing the chest's fascinating career is here reproduced. The chest was purchased by us from the Sweet family.

For Sarah Smith, dau. of 'Deacon John' one of the six John Smiths in Hadley at the end of the 17th century. She was born Nov. 9, 1698, married Samuel Kellogg, her cousin, May 22,1724. The chest came down the Kellogg line, reaching Esther Smith Kellogg who married Gen. Martin Field in 1802, and took this as her dowry chest to Newfane, Vermont, where General Field became an attorney of prominence, grandfather of Eugene Field. About 1877 an exhibition of furniture was held in Newfane, in which an English origin was ascribed to this piece, was reported in the Vermont Phoenix. Then initials considered to stand for Samuel Smith the founder. In the inventory of the estate of Samuel Kellogg, as "prized" Sept. 11, 1741, this piece is listed as follows:

"for a Chist 01-05-00"

Sarah Kellogg, the widow, is named as Administratrix and signs "her mark" to bond. Draker pulls late. Note scrolls at rail and drawer centers.

Owner: Stanley Sweet, New York.
Inspected May 15, 1928.

P3858 Pair of iron and brass andirons, the brass tops are diamond faceted with a smaller faceted diamond above, the turned iron base with bulbous shaft, spurred legs ending in penny feet and iron backstop is of exceptional refinement, Rhode Island circa 1740-1770.

Ht. 23″ Dp. 18″

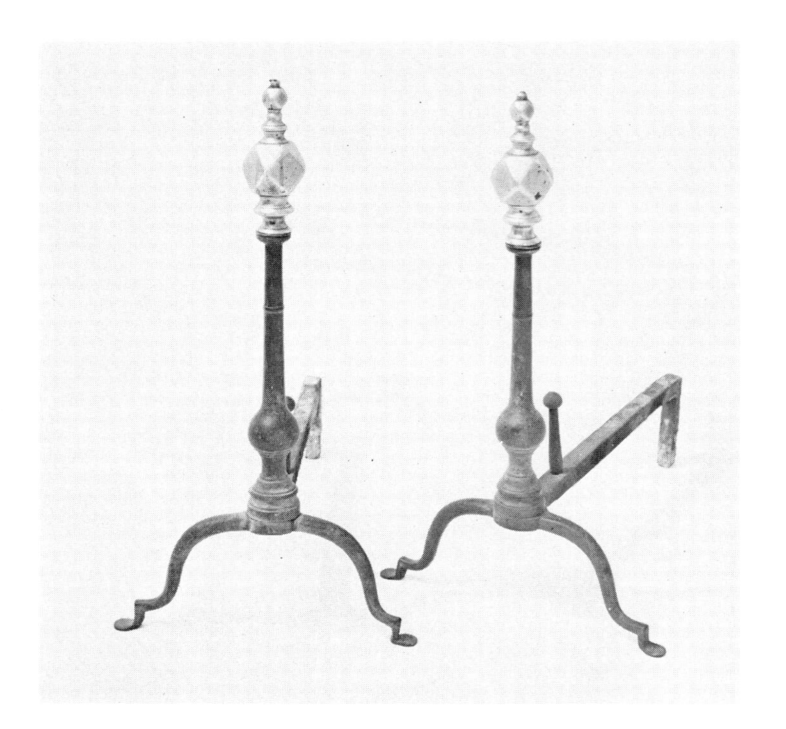

P3868 Early Queen Anne maple Spanish foot side chair, ball and ring frontal stretcher and bulbous ring turned side stretchers, spooned back with moulded stiles and horned yoke crest rail, dark brown finish retaining traces of old black paint, Salem, Massachusetts, circa 1720-1740. Descended in the family of Timothy Pickering of Salem.

Ht. 42″

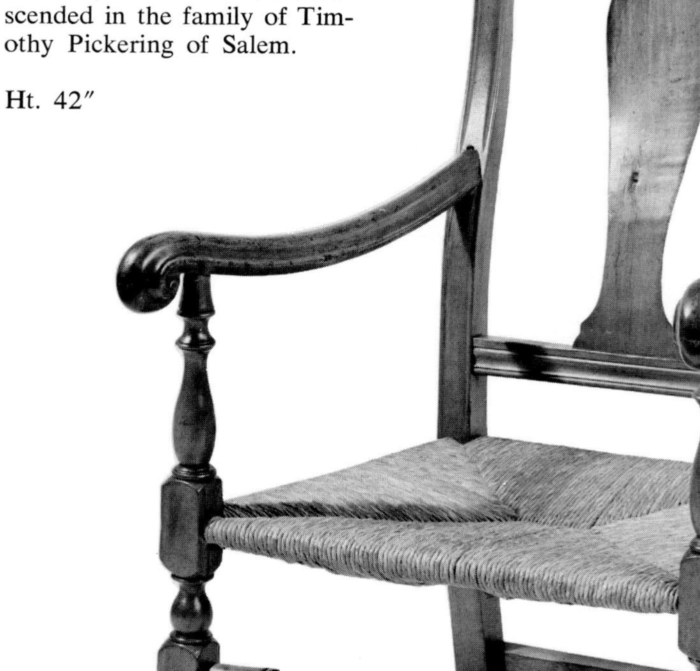

P3818 Queen Anne maple Spanish foot armchair, tall, stately proportions, moulded serpentine arms with flaring scrolled terminals, horned yoke crest, warm ruddy patina, fine spooned profile, North Shore, Massachusetts, circa 1730-1760. This chair exhibits more careful modelling than the usual example.

Ht. 43″ Wd. 24½″

FROM THE PIONEER GREENWOOD COLLECTION

P3827 Rare early maple folding bed with original crane canopy, retains the original brick red paint, headboard, diagonal braces, tester frame, and rails (except head rail), Massachusetts circa 1740-1760. This is the only intact example we have seen for sale in at least 25 years.

From the pioneer Greenwood Colllection. Part of the Greenwood Collection was donated to the Smithsonian Institution where it is now on view.

Ht. 7′ 5″ Lg. 6′ 5½″ Wd. 53″

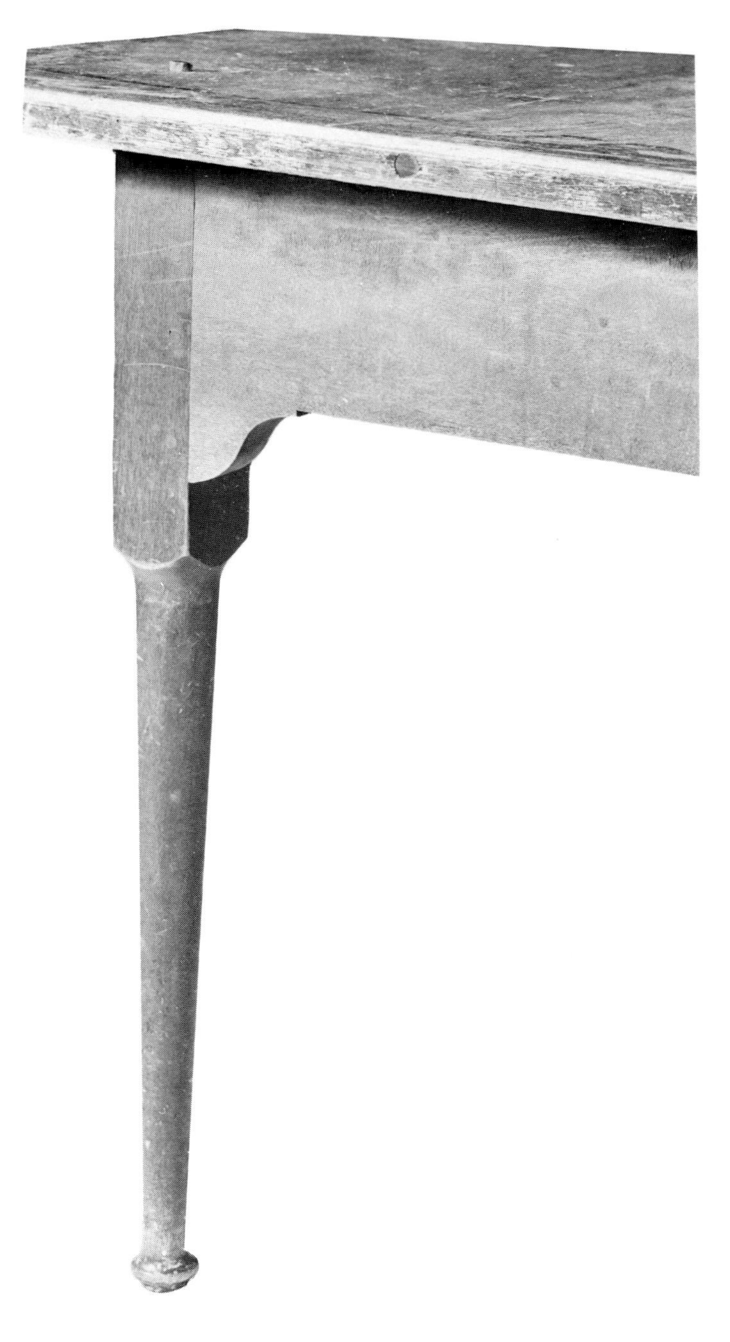

P3821 Queen Anne cherry communion table with a one board top over 13 feet in length, cleated ends, turned legs ending in pad feet with cyma curved scrolled corners related to conventional porringer top tea tables, one side contains a drawer with thumbnail borders, original finish and condition, Rhode Island or Connecticut circa 1740-1760. This table was perhaps the outstanding item of the pioneer Greenwood Collection and was purchased from the heirs. Examples donated by Mrs. Greenwood are on exhibit in the Smithsonian Institution.

Ht. 28½″ Lg. 13′ 4¾″ Wd. 31″

P3861 Chippendale walnut high chest of drawers with panelled sides and arched top drawers, original brasses with spurred bales; narrow quarter columns, ogee bracket feet, Chester County, Pennsylvania, circa 1750-1780.

Chester County characteristics of this piece include the arched top drawers, deeply chamfered side panels and the inset ogee bracket feet. The sides of the case extend to the floor serving as supports for the feet.

Ht. 68¼″ Wd. 44½″ Dp. 24″

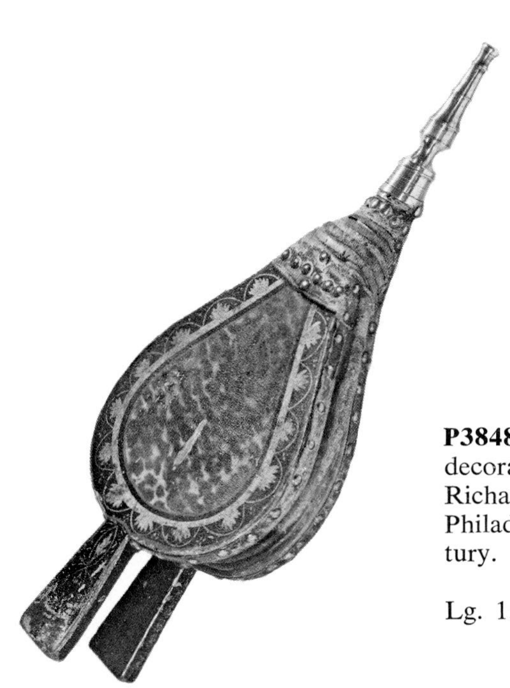

P3848 Pair of bellows with stencilled decoration bearing the label Eckstein and Richardson, No. 36 North Third Street, Philadelphia, first half of the 19th century.

Lg. 15¾″ Wd. 5¾″

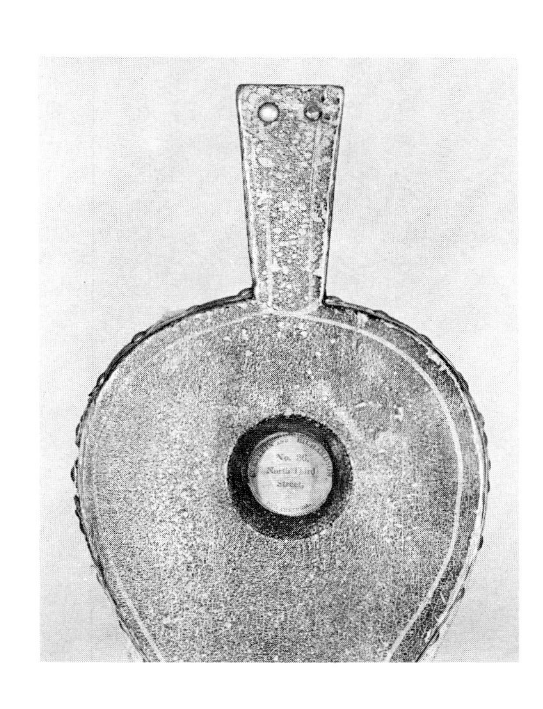

P3859 Queen Anne walnut wardrobe on frame, the frame with four drawers and original bale brasses is supported on shell carved cabriole legs with drake feet and finely scrolled apron with fishtail center and ends, arch panelled doors in upper case with arched moulding above and flanked by fluted quarter columns, fine patina, Pennsylvania circa 1740-1760. A wardrobe on cabriole frame is rare or possibly unique.

Ht. 74¼″ Wd. 52″ Dp. 20½″

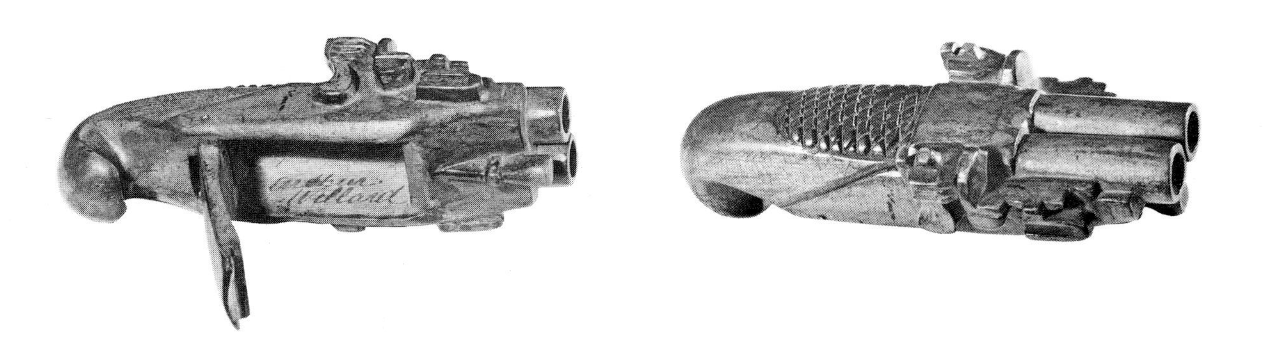

P3833 Cherry snuff box in the form of a double barrelled flint lock pistol, the base has a hinged lid with the contemporary inscription Arthur Willard in the compartment, warm amber patina, American late 18th century.

Lg. 5¼″

3899 Early maple and pine tavern table, the rectangular top with original cleated ends has a fine early aspect, the base with its exceptional disc and bulbous turned feet retains the original blue paint, Connecticut circa 1700-1720. From the pioneer Greenwood Collection.

Ht. 26½″ Wd. 48″ Dp. 30¾″

P3810 Queen Anne walnut dropleaf table, round top, cabriole legs, pad feet, shaped apron, rich brown color, Massachusetts circa 1740-1760.

Ht. 27″ Lg. 42″ Wd. open 41″
closed 15″

P3819 Chippendale birch oxbow bureau of desirable small size, bracket feet, fine brown color, Salem, Massachusetts, circa 1760-1780.

Ht. 34″ Wd. 38″ Dp. 20″

P3839 Pair of brass urn top andirons, square plinths with basket engraved fronts and rosette paterae engraved sides, scrolled bases, spurred cabriole legs with pad feet, urn tops with drapery engraving, probably by James Wittingham, New York circa 1790-1800.

Ht. 26″ Wd. 12″ Dp. 20½″

P3877 Queen Anne cherry lowboy of desirable small size, fan carved center drawer, gracefully modelled cabriole legs, beautiful light amber patina, Connecticut circa 1750-1770.

Ht. 29″ Wd. 32¾″ Dp. 22⅛″

P3875 Chippendale mahogany tripod candlestand, the cabriole legs have C-scrolled marginal carving and end in finely sculptured claw and ball feet, urn column, the oval top tilts on a boxed frame, choice light brown patina, Boston or Salem, Massachusetts, circa 1760-1780.

The base and the ball and claw feet of this table bear a close relationship to the Derby fire screen carved by McIntire, illustrated Randall "American Furniture" plate 114A.

Ht. 27⅝″ Top 20⅝″ x 15¼″

P3841 Queen Anne walnut corner chair, overupholstered balloon seat, cabriole front leg ending in pad foot, side and rear legs with pad feet intact, turned cross stretchers, inverted vase shaped splats, mellow light brown patina, Massachusetts circa 1740-1760.

Ht. 31″ Wd. 28″ Dp. 26″

P3881 Chippendale mahogany dropleaf table, squared cabriole legs ending in claw and ball feet with elongated talons in the Newport manner, bulged scrolled apron, light brown color, Newport, Rhode Island, circa 1750-1770.

Ht. 27¾″ Wd. 14″ closed
Lg. 42″ 42″ open

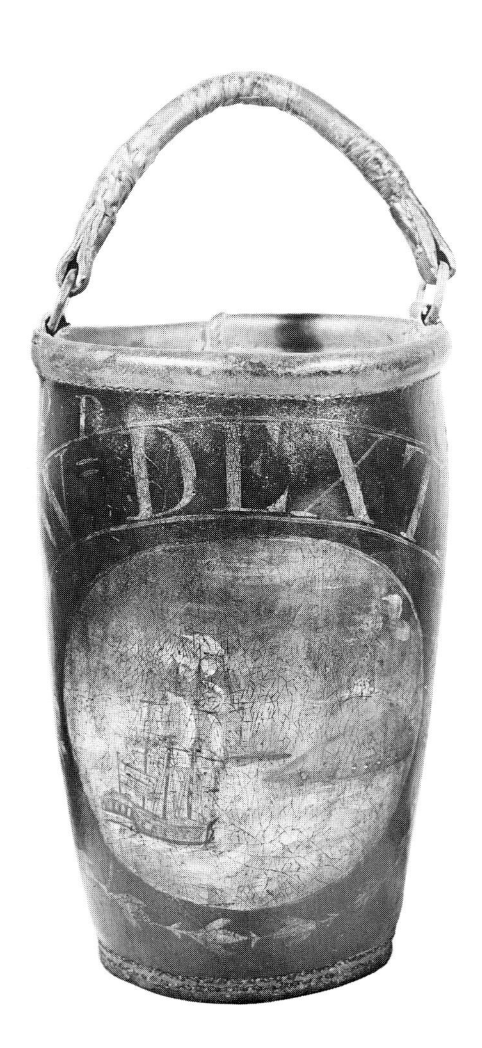

P3910 Decorated fire bucket depicting a ship bearing the American flag, inscribed "Edw — DEXTER — 1794." Edward Dexter was a wealthy ship owner of Providence born 1770. His mansion in Providence was once occupied by Charles Pendleton and served as the source for the architectural scheme of the Rhode Island School of Design. This bucket was purchased from the Dexter homestead.

Ht. 13¼″ Diam. 9″

P3897 Decorated leather fire bucket depicting American eagle holding in his beak a banner inscribed "Washington Fire Club, Gideon Tucker 1803," Boston or Salem, Massachusetts.

Ht. 11″ Diam. 8⅜″

P3896 Decorated leather fire bucket depicting a burning ship and inscribed Joseph Chapman 1796 in wreath border, branded "I. Fenno," Massachusetts, dated 1796. John Fenno was a leather maker in Boston who specialized in making fire buckets for the prominent fire societies of Boston and Salem.

Ht. 13¼″ Diam 9″

P3890 Queen Anne maple Spanish foot armchair, finely moulded arms with scrolled terminals, conventional Queen Anne yoke crested back with good serpentine profile, ball and ring turned frontal stretcher, mellow light brown patina, Massachusetts circa 1730-1750.

Ht. 41½″ Wd. 24″ Dp. 24″

P3895 Chippendale cherry pipe box, one drawer with thumbnail borders, original cyma shaped sides and crest of beautiful outline, fine bronze patina, New England circa 1750-1780.

Ht. 21¾″ Wd. 6¼″ Dp. 5½″

P3815 Large burl bowl with raised rim, exceptional quality and condition, American, 18th century.

Ht. 6¼″ Dia. 17″

P3860 Chippendale mahogany oxbow bureau with blocked ends, rare double ogee bracket feet, choice nut brown patina, Boston or Charlestown, Massachusetts, circa 1760-1780. A labelled Frothingham block front chest-on-chest with related double ogee bracket feet is illustrated Frontispiece ANTIQUES November 1952.

Ht. 30½″ Wd. 38″ Dp. 20½″

P3483 Hepplewhite mahogany mirror with scrolled crest and base, carved and gilded phoenix bird silhouetted in crest, line inlaid and carved and gilded mirror border, New York circa 1780-1800.

Ht. 45″ Wd. 24″

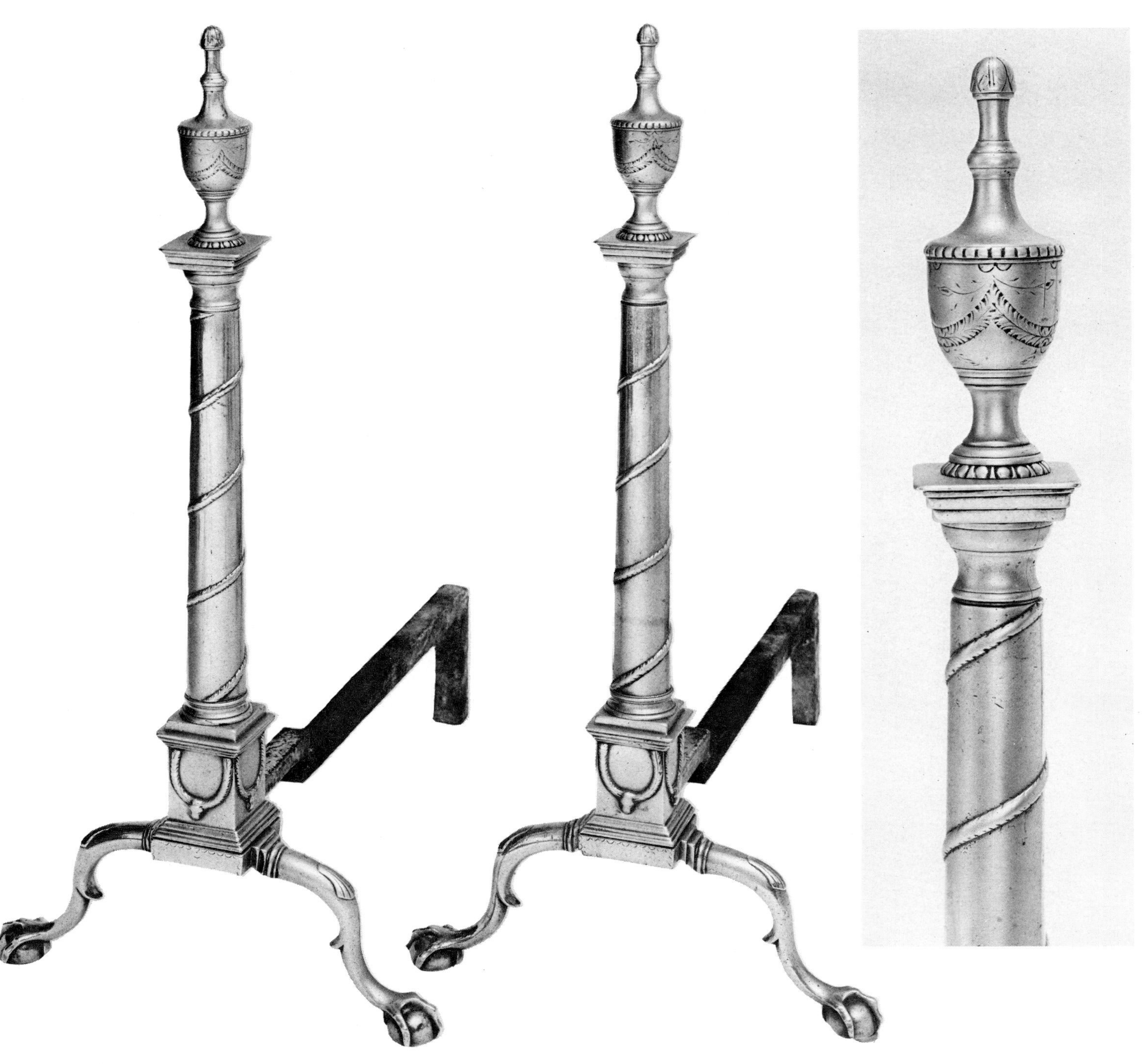

P3882 Pair of Chippendale ball and claw foot andirons with shell ornamented knees, square plinths with wreath and ram's heads in relief, the columns with spiral bands, engraved urn tops with gadrooned bases and borders and with petalled finials, attributed to Daniel King, Philadelphia circa 1760-1780. These superb andirons bear a distinct relationship to the priceless hairy paw andirons illustrated in Hornor's "Blue Book of Philadelphia Furniture," pl. 106. The plinths of both pairs have wreaths and ram's heads. Also hooks at the base of the plinths give evidence of a missing gadrooned base border as appears on the hairy paw andirons.

Several features appearing on the signed Daniel King pair of andirons in the Henry F. du Pont Winterthur Museum are evident in this pair to support the attribution to Daniel King. We consider this handsome pair to be one of the most beautiful designs produced in the Colonies.

Ht. 28″ Wd. 13″ Dp. 22″

P3871 Queen Anne San Domingan mahogany lowboy, boldly serpentine cabriole legs of squared outline with scrolled knee brackets, pad feet with flaring platforms, the apron is a masterful series of undulating scrolls with diamond center cutout under the fan carved drawer, scrolls repeating in a reduced scale on sides. The outline formed by the beautifully modelled cabriole legs, brackets and apron design result in one of the most beautiful and creative compositions on an American Queen Anne lowboy. Original brasses and dark brown patina. The top retains its original glue blocks with the name Stephen ——————, in contemporary chalk on underside. Salem, Massachusetts, circa 1750-1770.

The piece descended in the Broughton family of Salem, Massachusetts. Salem features are the flat shelf scrolled knee returns and the diamond center apron cutout.

Ht. 30¾″ Wd. 35″ Dp. 22½″

P3849 Queen Anne San Domingan mahogany corner chair, one cabriole leg with pointed knee, pad foot and flaring trumpet platform, turned side and rear legs ending in pad feet with flaring trumpet platforms, cyma scrolled aprons, interlaced splat, fine bronze patina; the careful craftsmanship and the modelling from dense mahogany show the hand of a superior artisan, Salem, Massachusetts, circa 1750-1770.

This chair descended in the Broughton family of Salem, Mass. and appears to be by the same hand as P3871 (lowboy).

Ht. 30¼″ Wd. 28½″

P3873 Chippendale mahogany tray top tea table, beautifully scrolled apron on all four sides with scrolled knee returns, cabriole legs ending in finely sculptured claw and ball feet, applied tray top with notched corners, with retaining moulding below, rich dark brown patina, Newport, Rhode Island, circa 1750-1780. The top is of double thickness extending below the surface of the top in the same manner as the Newport slipper foot table group. The supporting blocks of the legs and frame are virtually all intact.

Ht. 27½″ Lg. 29¼″ Dp. 19¾″

P3838 Queen Anne walnut balloon seat side chair with hooped stiles, violin splat, cabriole legs with marginal C-scrolled knee borders, cyma curved scrolled apron, cyma curved flat stretchers, attributed to Job Townsend, Newport, Rhode Island, circa 1740-1750. A related set of chairs made by Job Townsend for the Eddy family 1743 were sold in the Sack 100 Important American Antiques Catalogue 1932, #80.

Ht. 40¾″

P3891 Chippendale Walnut "Martha Washington" mirror with original carved and gilded eagle ornament and side leaves; the finely sculptured eagle is perched on a scrolled volute flanked by a broken arch pediment with floral carved terminal pendants, the scrollboard with gilt cartouche tracery, original bevelled mirror glass, American or English circa 1750-1780. Descended in the Sweet family.

Ht. 54″ Wd. 28½″

P3808 Queen Anne curly walnut lowboy, case with one long drawer over row of divided drawers, cyma scrolled apron, graceful cabriole legs ending in drake feet, moulded top with notched corners, Philadelphia or vicinity circa 1750-1760. The beauty of the figured walnut grain is enhanced by a warm ruddy patina of great depth and mellowness.

Ht. 29¼″ Wd. 34¼″ Dp. 22″

P3842 Queen Anne walnut diminutive mirror, scrolled crest centered by pressed gilded shell, original glass and finish, American or English circa 1740-1760.

Ht. 16¼″ Wd. 9¾″

P3900 Chippendale mahogany mirror of important size and in the finest original state, scrolled crest and base; carved and gilded phoenix silhouetted in crest, American or English circa 1760-1780.

Ht. 42″ Wd. 24″

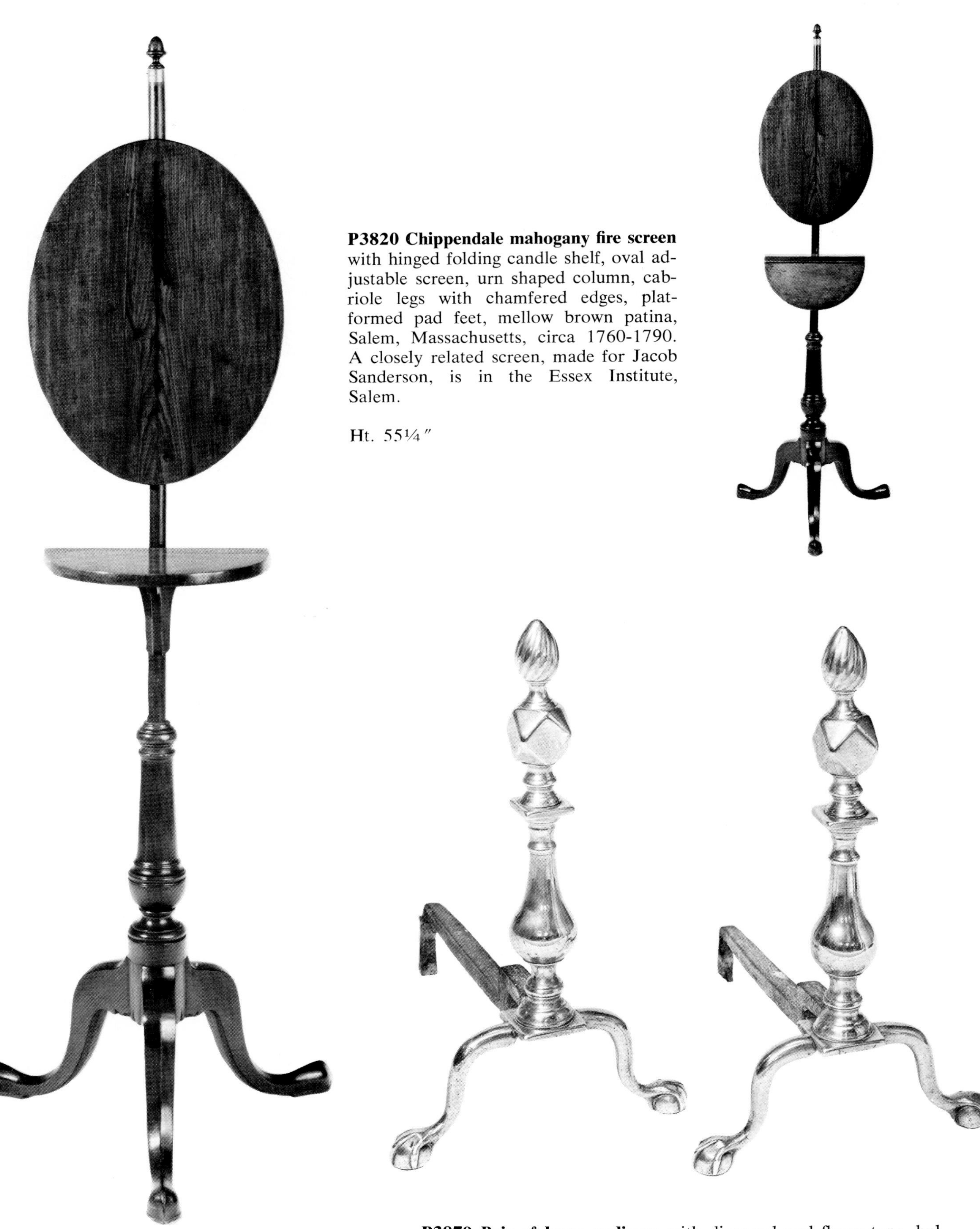

P3820 Chippendale mahogany fire screen with hinged folding candle shelf, oval adjustable screen, urn shaped column, cabriole legs with chamfered edges, platformed pad feet, mellow brown patina, Salem, Massachusetts, circa 1760-1790. A closely related screen, made for Jacob Sanderson, is in the Essex Institute, Salem.

Ht. 55¼″

P3879 Pair of brass andirons with diamond and flame tops, bulbous turned columns, square plinths, cabriole legs with claw and ball feet, school of Paul Revere, Massachusetts, or Rhode Island, circa 1750-1770.

Ht. 20½″ Wd. 12″ Dp. 16¼″

P3840 Rare pair of Chippendale mahogany mirrors with finely scrolled crests and bases, the crests with silhouetted carved and gilded phoenix birds facing each other, moulded mirror borders with notched corners and carved and gilded inner borders, probably Massachusetts circa 1760-1780. The identical inscription on the back of each mirror reads "22 x 13 Edge & Bird." This represents the measurement of carving and gilding on each mirror.

Ht. 34¼" Wd. 19¼"

P3811 Queen Anne rectangular tea table, raised dish rim with notched corners, base of exceptional graceful silhouette formed by a shallow scrolled apron and exquisitely slender cabriole legs with C-scrolled terminals; the beauty of the rare design is enhanced by a beautiful mellow brown patina, Rhode Island circa 1740-1760.

Ht. 28″ Lg. 30½″ Wd. 19¾″

P3870 Queen Anne mahogany blockfront slant top desk of rare small size and early date; the formation of the blocking with domed top drawer is related to the secretary desk signed by Job Coit, Jr., Boston, Massachusetts, 1738, in the Henry F. du Pont Winterthur Museum. The blocking extends onto the bracket feet with fine cyma scrolled inner outlines and center pendant. The amphitheater interior is centered by a fan carved door simulating drawer fronts and conceals a removable compartment with secret drawers. Attributed to Job Coit, Jr., Boston, Massachusetts, circa 1735-1745.

The beauty of the piece is enhanced by a superb mellow brown patina. Evidences of the early date are shown by the small size, original engraved bat wing brasses, the short pullout slides and the broad facades of the bracket feet.

Ht. 42″ Wd. 36″ Dp. 20″ Wtg. Lvl. 31½″

P3792 Carved spread eagle perched on rock formation, important size and great vitality, retaining the old brown paint, supported on marbleized pine base, American early 19th century.

Ht. 29¼″ Wd. 39¼″ Dp. 16¼″

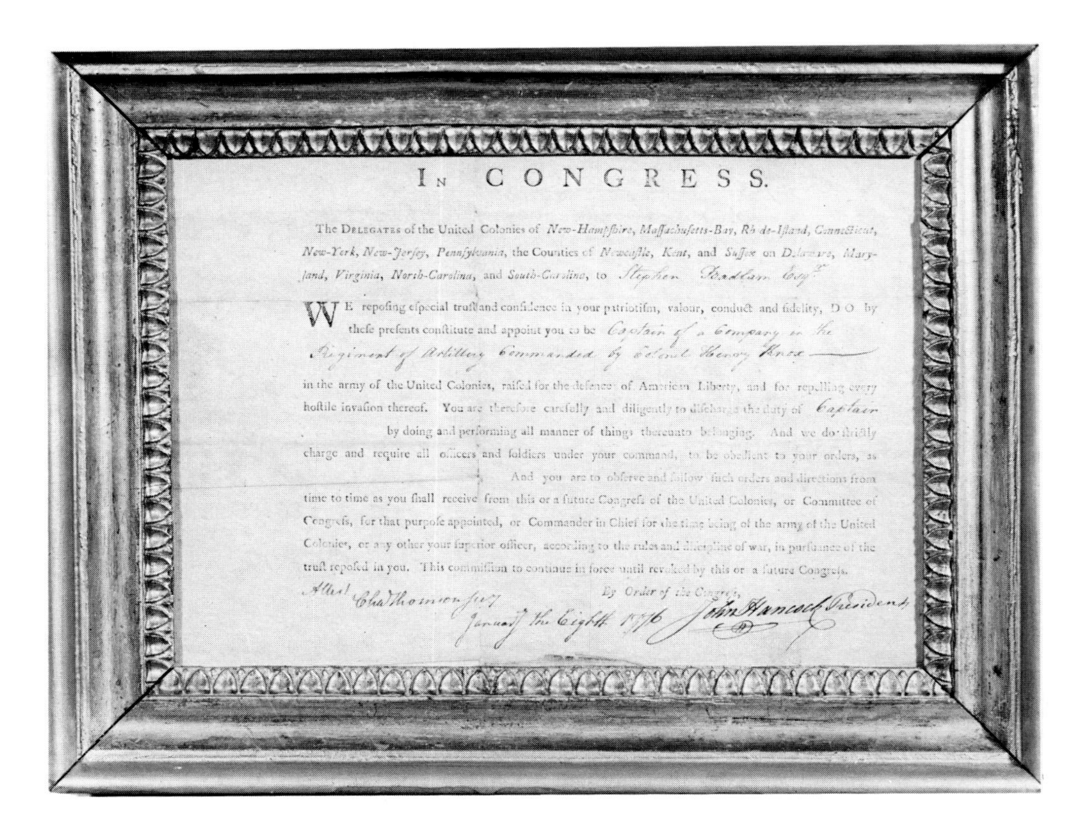

IN CONGRESS.

The DELEGATES of the United Colonies of *New-Hampshire*, *Massachusetts-Bay*, *Rhode-Island*, *Connecticut*, *New-York*, *New-Jersey*, *Pennsylvania*, the Counties of *Newcastle*, *Kent*, and *Sussex* on *Delaware*, *Maryland*, *Virginia*, *North-Carolina*, and *South-Carolina*, to Stephen Badlam Esqr.

WE reposing especial trust and confidence in your patriotism, valour, conduct and fidelity, DO by these presents constitute and appoint you to be Captain of a Company in the Regiment of Artillery Commanded by Colonel Henry Knox — in the army of the United Colonies, raised for the defence of American Liberty, and for repelling every hostile invasion thereof. You are therefore carefully and diligently to discharge the duty of Captain by doing and performing all manner of things thereunto belonging. And we do strictly charge and require all officers and soldiers under your command, to be obedient to your orders, as And you are to observe and follow such orders and directions from time to time as you shall receive from this or a future Congress of the United Colonies, or Committee of Congress, for that purpose appointed, or Commander in Chief for the time being of the army of the United Colonies, or any other your superior officer, according to the rules and discipline of war, in pursuance of the trust reposed in you. This commission to continue in force until revoked by this or a future Congress.

Attest Chas Thomson Secy

By Order of the Congress,

January the Eighth 1776 John Hancock President

P3850 Commission appointing Stephen Badlam, Captain of a Company in the Regiment of Artillery Commanded by Colonel Henry Knox, signed by John Hancock, President of the Continental Congress, January 8, 1776. In carved and gilded period frame.

Stephen Badlam, the famous Boston cabinetmaker (1751-1815) "received a commission in the artillery shortly after the outbreak of the Revolution and when obliged to resign because of illness had become a captain" . . . from Bjerkoe "The Cabinetmakers of America," page 35.

Ht. 12¾″ Wd. 16¼″

P3837 Set of six Chippendale mahogany side chairs, interlaced Gothic splats, serpentine crests with C-scrolled ears, moulded stiles, square legs with beaded edges, H-stretchers, Philadelphia circa 1750-1780.

Ht. 38″

P3803 Pair of Hepplewhite mahogany D-shaped card tables, finely matched crotch veneered frames, tops with cancave moulded edges, beaded apron borders, fine bronze patina, Philadelphia circa 1780-1800. Descended in the Sharp-Leedom families of Philadelphia.

Ht. 29½″ Wd. 36″ Dp. 17¾″

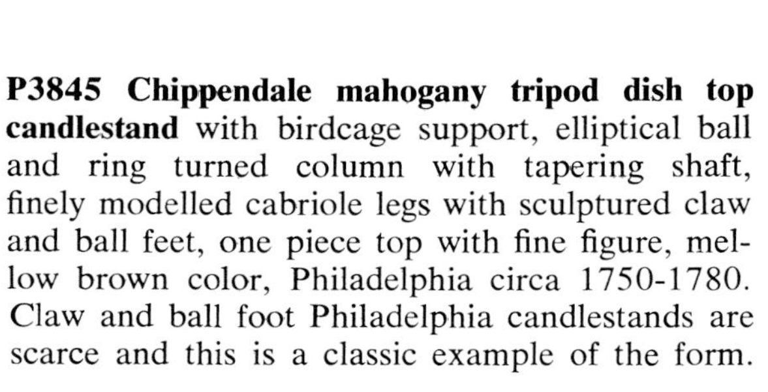

P3845 Chippendale mahogany tripod dish top candlestand with birdcage support, elliptical ball and ring turned column with tapering shaft, finely modelled cabriole legs with sculptured claw and ball feet, one piece top with fine figure, mellow brown color, Philadelphia circa 1750-1780. Claw and ball foot Philadelphia candlestands are scarce and this is a classic example of the form.

Ht. 29″ Dia. 23¾″

P3807 Set of twelve Sheraton mahogany dining chairs consisting of two arm and 10 side chairs, moulded flaring slats with carved terminals, the crests with fluted raised panels, tapered legs with spade feet, New York circa 1800-1810. Choice color and excellent state of preservation.

Ht. 37″

A set of twelve chairs of this design but with outsplayed legs is in the Du Pont Dining Room, The Henry F. du Pont Winterthur Museum. Two armchairs and five side chairs of this group are from one matching set. The other five chairs are singles and pairs from other sets of the same design and quality.

A TOWNSEND MASTERPIECE

P3855 Chippendale mahogany card table, frame and conforming top with blocked center and squared corners, superbly modelled squared cabriole legs with broad leaf and floral carving, open talon claw and ball feet with high ridged ankles; both rear legs pivot, choice original golden patina, attributed to John Townsend, Newport, Rhode Island, circa 1760-1765.

This table is identical to the famous Redwood Library table donated to the Library by Ellen Townsend and illustrated "The John Brown House, Loan Exhibition" Catalog #34. A closely related table bears the inscription "John Townsend, Newport 1762."

This table descended in the Lyman family of Boston and Newport. It was purchased by us from the estate of a descendant.

Ht. 27½″ Wd. 34½″ Dp. 17″

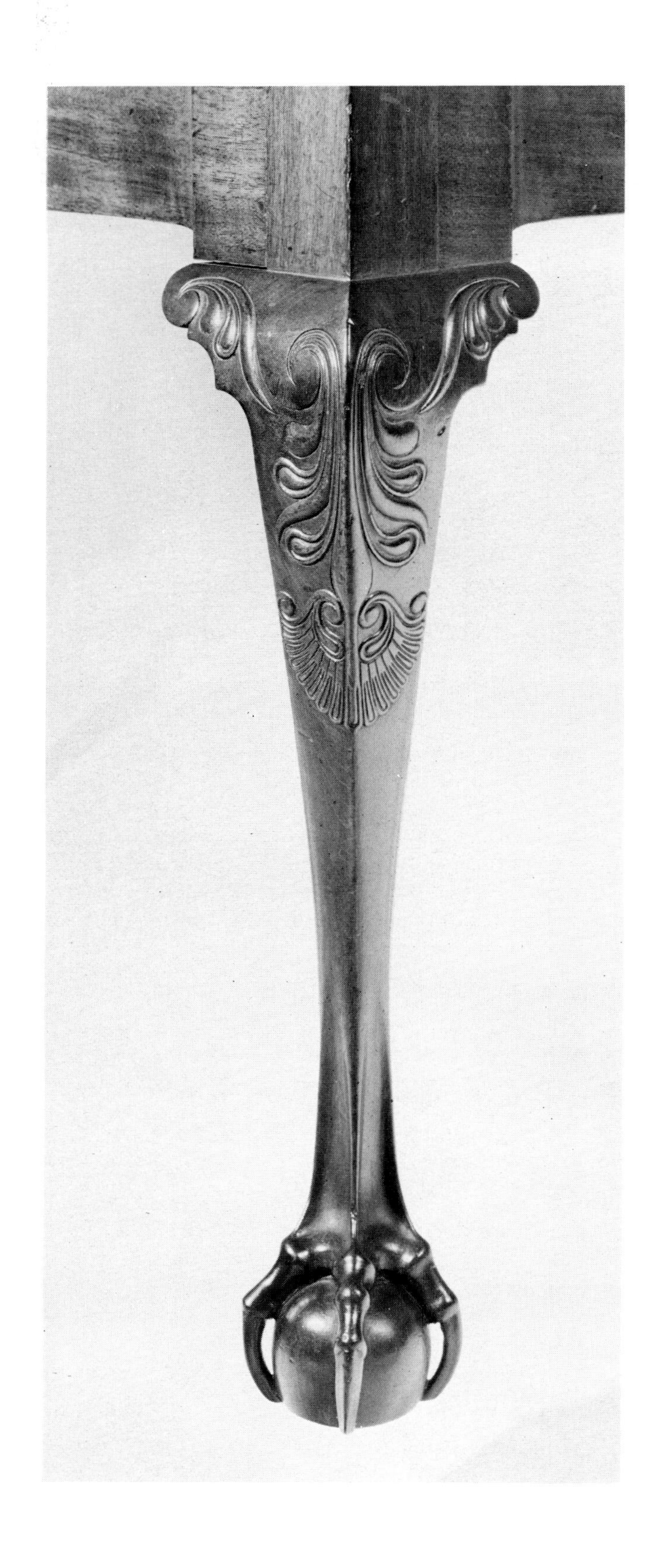

P3831 Hepplewhite mahogany bow front sideboard, tapered legs with bellflower inlay, inlaid oval shell paterae and large buds on each stile, serpentine arched apron with bold inlaid center shell, one long drawer above flanked by deep cupboard drawers with oval crossbanded centers; original octagonal chased brasses and superb mellow brown patina, Baltimore or Annapolis, Maryland, circa 1780-1800.

This sideboard was purchased from direct descendants of the first owner, William Blair, Jr., of Carlisle, Pennsylvania, who furnished us with voluminous family documents. From this material the following line of descent is offered:

1. William Blair, Jr.—son of William Blair I—born October 14, 1740—died March 21, 1792—married Sarah Holmes, born February 1763—died June 19, 1827. They were married in 1784 and lived in Carlisle.

2. Andrew Blair—son of William Blair, Jr.—born April 10, 1789—died July 21, 1860—married Elizabeth Hays, born April 10, 1792—died January 2, 1843. They were married March 31, 1812.

3. William Blair IV—son of Andrew Blair—born April 13, 1815—died October 12, 1896—married Ellen Cayne in 1838.

4. Ellen Blair—daughter of William Blair IV—born November 22, 1846—died May 28, 1904—married Samuel Woods Sterrett, born December 31, 1840. They were married at Blair residence, Carlisle, on February 28, 1873.

5. Surviving children of Samuel Woods Sterrett and Ellen (Blair) Sterrett—Mary Woods Sterrett and John Scott Sterrett.

Ht. 37½″ Lg. 69½″ Dp. 27½″

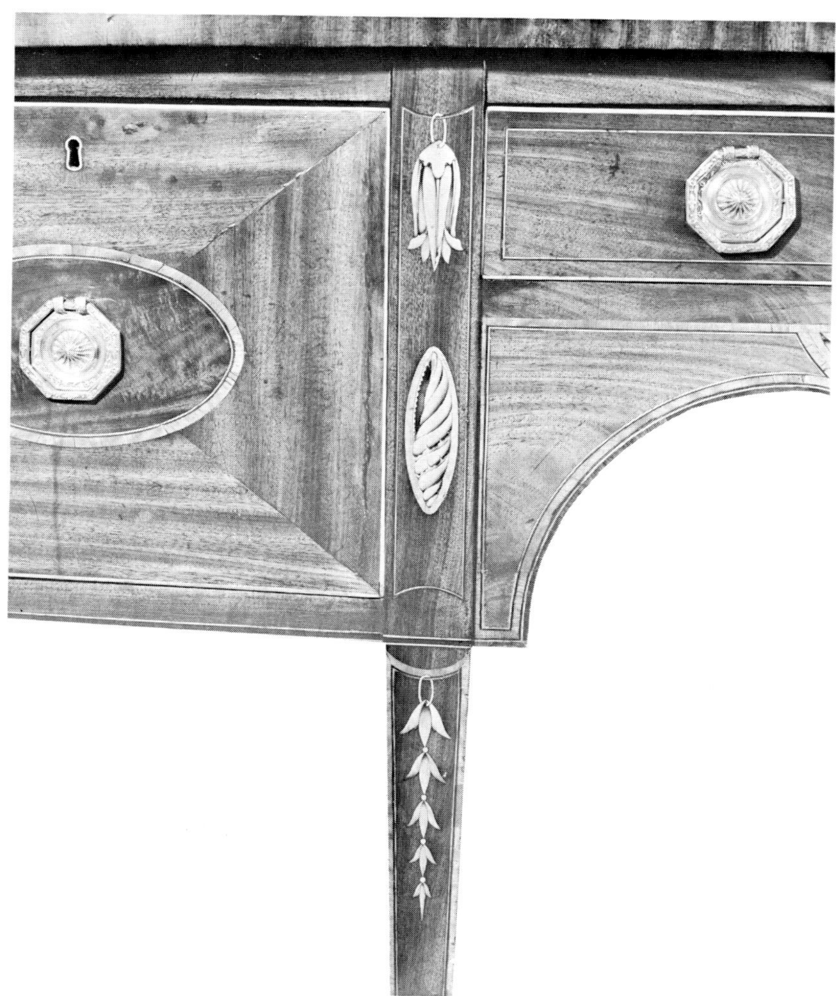

P3853 Chippendale San Domingan mahogany block front slant top desk, ball and claw feet with acanthus carved knees, brackets and finely carved center pendant; the interior of blocked drawers with fan carved center door flanked by flame pilastered document drawers, concave blocked end drawers, the left row capped by fan carving, the right row with domed crest, Massachusetts circa 1760–1780. Descended in the family of Lemuel Haskins and purchased by us from the Haskins family.

Ht. 44¼″ Wd. 42″ Dp. 22″ Wtg. Lvl. 33″

P3884 Queen Anne curly walnut bonnet top highboy, fan carved center drawer in upper and lower case sections; the end drawers flanking the top fan carved drawer are shaped to conform to the line of the arch, original brasses, mellow light brown patina, attributed to Benjamin Frothingham, Charlestown, Massachusetts, circa 1750-1760.

Comparison of the thumbnail bordered fan carving, the inner arch outline and the shaped upper end drawers with the signed Frothingham highboy in the Henry F. du Pont Winterthur Museum (see "Fine Points of Furniture, Early American" page 185) lend credence to the attribution.

Ht. 7′5″ Wd. 40″ Dp. 21″

A NEW YORK MASTERPIECE

P3852 Chippendale mahogany five legged claw and ball foot card table, deep serpentine front and sides with square candle corners, narrow frame with concave and convex gadrooned border on front apron only, the frame supported on four gracefully shaped cabriole legs with a fifth swing leg in rear concealing an original secret drawer, the front legs and knee brackets are carved with assymetrical C-scrolls and acanthus leafage; the top is felt lined with recessed candle corners and scoop, choice mellow brown patina, New York circa 1760-1780.

The New York serpentine card table is considered the masterpiece of the New York pre-Revolutionary era. A scholarly presentation of this group by Morrison H. Heckscher appears in ANTIQUES May 1973, pages 974-983. This form with the narrow skirt and graceful cabriole legs relates to Type II in the Heckscher article and appears to be by the same hand as the Beekman tables in the New York Historical Society.

This table descended in the Varick family and was purchased from the estate of a direct descendant.

Ht. 27¾″ Wd. 34″ Dp. 16½″

P3791 Hepplewhite mahogany grandfather clock of desirable small size, the exceptional case has black and white fan quadrants in the door and base sections as well as in the corners of the hood door, the quarter columns and fluted hood columns are capped by finely wrought brass Corinthian capitals, the waist door is centered by an inlaid spray, the enamel moon dial has two bluebirds on the face and is inscribed "Nath. Edwards, Acton," the contemporary inscription inside case, "Jason Richards, Woburn," is probably that of the case maker, the beauty is enhanced by a warm mellow brown patina, made by Nathan Edwards, Acton, Massachusetts, circa 1800-1810.

Ht. 7′5¾″ Wd. 18″ Dp. 9″

P3388 Hepplewhite mahogany tambour sideboard of rare small size bearing all the characteristics of the work of John Seymour and Son, i.e., the ivory escutcheon in the scrolled center bracket containing a lock to lock the tambours, the scrolled corner brackets and the inlaid columnar pilasters flanking the tambour shutters, and traces of the distinctive blue-green paint in the cupboard compartments. The top drawers also contain oval ivory escutcheons. The legs are tapered with banded cuffs and additional taper below; the carefully selected mahogany has taken on a satiny bronze patina typical of the Seymour shop. Attributed to John Seymour and Son, Boston, Massachusetts, circa 1790-1800.

Ht. 40½″ Wd. 48½″ Dp. 22¾″

P3878 Pair of Queen Anne walnut side chairs, straight seats with scalloped aprons, cabriole legs and pad feet, cylindrical rear legs, turned stretchers, Massachusetts circa 1740-1770.

Ht. 40½″

P3876 Chippendale tripod candle-stand fashioned of the densest San Domingan mahogany, square moulded stationary top with notched corners, column with small urn and tapering shaft, Newport, Rhode Island, circa 1750-1770.

Ht. 27¾″ Top 18¾″ x 19⅛″

P2578 Chippendale mahogany mirror of unique design, original two section glasses with carved and gilded borders and divider, the crest and base are formed of narrow tightly knit scrolls, each scroll pierced with circles and crescents, American or English circa 1760-1780.

Ht. 35″ Wd. 20″

P3832 Liverpool pitcher with historic scenes and patriotic inscriptions in black and white and color; one side depicting the American militia, the opposite side with vignettes of Samuel Adams and John Hancock with Washington memorial above, under the spout is American eagle, E. Pluribus Unum and inscription "Peace, Commerce and honest Friendship with All Nations, Entangling Alliances with none. JEFFERSON Anno Domini 1802." English for the American market, circa 1802.

Ht. 10″

Ref. McCauley 192 pl. VII, 155 pl. XXVIII

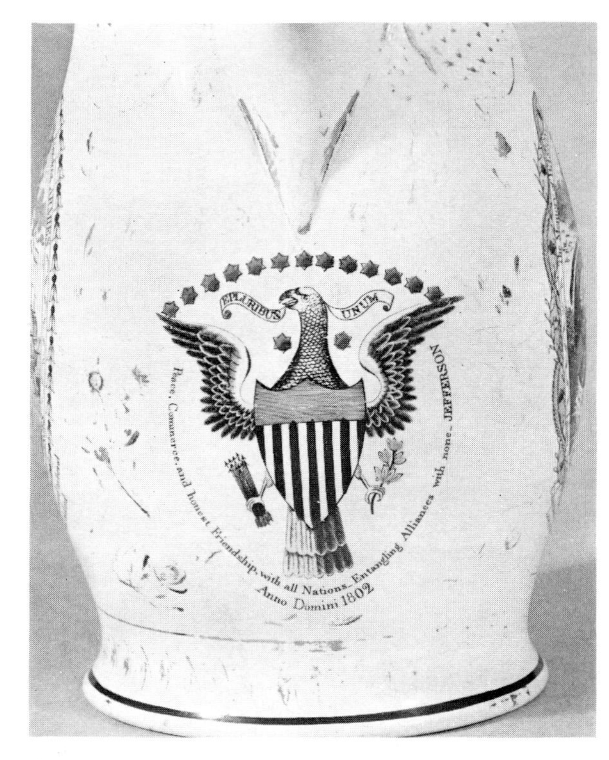

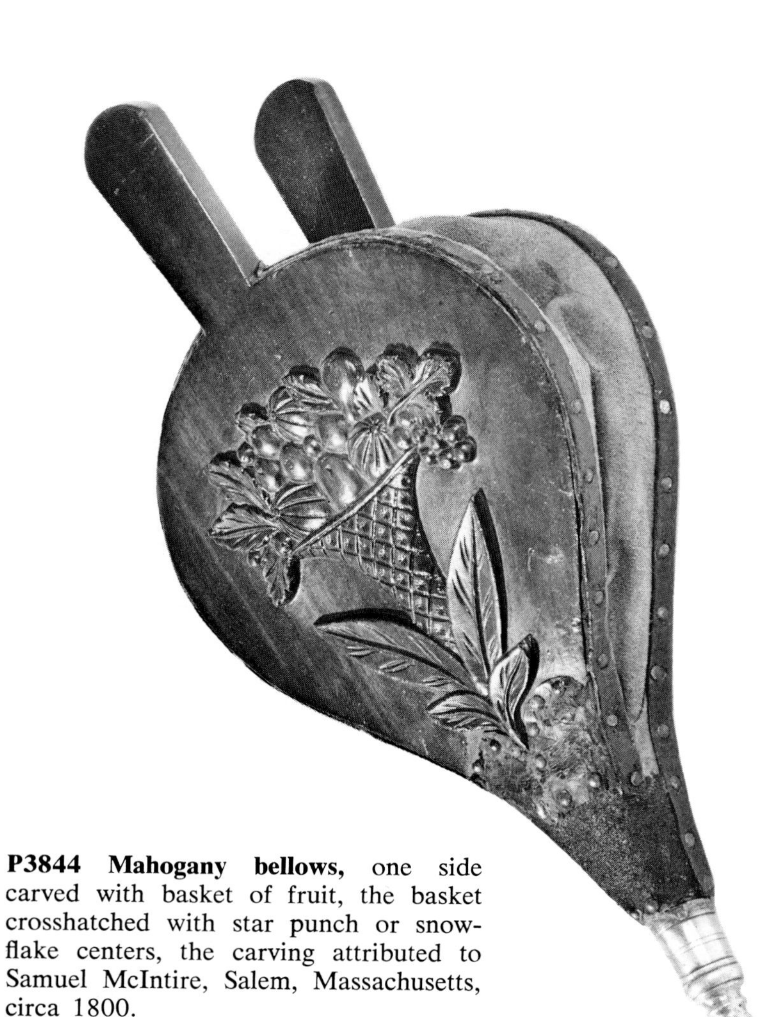

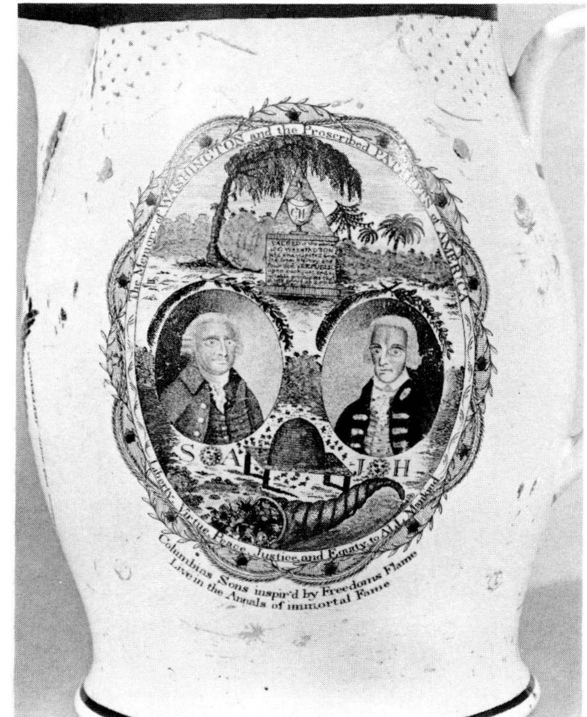

P3844 Mahogany bellows, one side carved with basket of fruit, the basket crosshatched with star punch or snowflake centers, the carving attributed to Samuel McIntire, Salem, Massachusetts, circa 1800.

The bellows originally belonged to John Winship (1754-1822) who fought in the Battle of Lexington and later moved to Salem. It was purchased by us from the great-great-grandson of John Winship.

Lg. 21½″ Wd. 9″

P3816 Queen Anne mahogany tea table of exceptional grace, slender turned tapering legs ending in platformed pad feet, cyma curved scrolled apron corners and center pendants, thin overhanging moulded edged top, beautiful golden patina, Rhode Island circa 1750-1760.

Ht. 27″ Lg. 28¼″ Wd. 21½″

P3805 Hepplewhite mahogany Martha Washington armchair or lolling chair, shaped serpentine arms, moulded arm supports, the moulding continuing on tapered legs of full length, H stretchers, fine craftsmanship and color, Massachusetts circa 1780-1800.

Ht. 43¾″ Wd. 26½″ Dp. 30″

P3866 Pair of Hepplewhite mahogany shield back side chairs with beautiful drapery and acanthus carved splats, finely shaped shields with pointed bases, tapered legs ending in spade feet, New York circa 1780-1800.

Ht. 39¼″

P3885 Hepplewhite mahogany serpentine front sideboard with recessed center cupboard and canted tapering center legs; the form is the exquisite grace and delicacy seen on the Karolik board in the Museum of Fine Arts, Boston, and the Fulton sideboard, considered the best form of American sideboard. The inlay of double line oval and circular panels on doors and cupboards is in understated taste and enhanced by a beautiful mellow brown patina. The brasses are original. New York circa 1780-1800.

Ht. 40″ Wd. 6′½″ Dp. 26¾″

P3830 Classical mahogany octagonal top card table with acanthus carved lyre pedestal, outsplayed acanthus carved legs ending in carved paw feet; top and frame is veneered with superbly figured flaming grain enhanced by a magnificent patina adding beauty to one of Phyfe's most successful designs; atributed to Duncan Phyfe, New York circa 1810-1820.

This table is apparently the mate to the Louis Guerineau Myers table in the Henry F. Du Pont Winterthur Museum illustrated in Nancy McClelland's "Masterpieces of Duncan Phyfe" plate 120. This table has the grained maple background panel to the lyre apparently missing from the Winterthur example.

Ht. 29½″ Wd. 36″ Dp. 18″

P3894 Classical mahogany sewing table with lyre side supports of rare delicacy, the lyres are contained by four reeded columns and supported on squared cross-banded bases with fire gilded brass end rosettes, outsplayed reeded legs ending in claw casters; the rectangular case has two drawers flanked by two vertical drawers retaining the original petalled brass knobs; the corners of the case are rounded with recessed birdseye maple panels and the bulged front sewing slide is flanked by spiral terminals; superb color and figured grain, attributed to Thomas Seymour circa 1810-1815. The attribution to Thomas Seymour is based on common characteristics appearing on this table and the documented sewing table made by Thomas Seymour for Ralph Haskins (Stoneman "John & Thomas Seymour" plate 151). Both show the rare petalled knobs, thumbnail bordered top edge, the sides with beaded bordered panels. The choice of fine woods and skillful craftsmanship is also indicative of the master. This table descended in the Lyman family of Boston and was purchased from the estate of a direct descendant. We consider it a masterpiece of the extremely small group of the Boston Classical school.

Further support to the attribution is based on one other table of related design and with identical lyres. That table was sold by us to Mr. and Mrs. Anthony Biddle. The Biddle table has the same petalled knobs, blue lined interior drawers and was made for Benjamin Hathorne, ship captain of Boston, 1774-1814.

Ht. 27½" Wd. 20" Dp. 14¾"

P3846 Pair of classical carved and gilded convex mirrors, high perched finely sculptured eagles facing each other on acanthus supports, flaring acanthus bases with attenuated bell-flower pendants, American or English circa 1800-1820.

Ht. 53″ Wd. 20″

P2065 Sheraton bow back sofa, bowed seat, reeded arms and bulbous reeded arm supports, bulbous reeded legs with elliptical turnings below, a graceful slender example retaining the original nut brown patina, Salem, Massachusettes, circa 1800-1810. This sofa is virtually identical to a sofa owned by us signed by Charles and John Lemon, Salem, Massachusetts, illustrated Sack Brochure #17, item 1084.

Ht. 34″ Wd. 6′7″ Dp. 27″

P3874 Hepplewhite mahogany shelf clock, kidney shaped dial inscribed Joseph Loring, the case with fan inlaid corners, French feet, the center plinth is flanked by beautifully scrolled fretwork, mellow light brown patina, made by Joseph Loring, Sterling, Massachusetts, circa 1795-1805.

Ht. 38¾″ Wd. 12¾″ Dp. 6¼″

P3793 Hepplewhite mahogany serving table, serpentine sides, the bowed center forms a drawer with diamond escutcheon and rosewood crossbanded apron fronts flanked by flame satinwood panels, slender tall tapering legs with line inlaid borders and cuffs, beautiful mellow light brown patina, Massachusetts circa 1780-1800.

Ex. Collection—the late Lansdell K. Christie

Illustrated Plate 38 "A Supplement to John and Thomas Seymour," Stoneman.

Ht. 34¾″ Wd. 36″ Dp. 17¾″

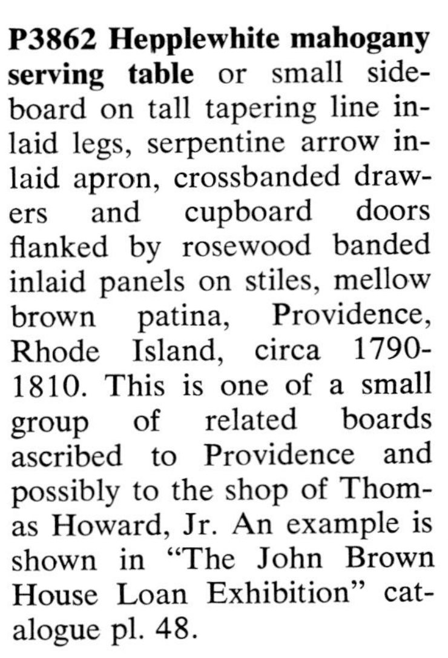

P3862 Hepplewhite mahogany serving table or small sideboard on tall tapering line inlaid legs, serpentine arrow inlaid apron, crossbanded drawers and cupboard doors flanked by rosewood banded inlaid panels on stiles, mellow brown patina, Providence, Rhode Island, circa 1790-1810. This is one of a small group of related boards ascribed to Providence and possibly to the shop of Thomas Howard, Jr. An example is shown in "The John Brown House Loan Exhibition" catalogue pl. 48.

Ht. 40″ Wd. 49½″

Dp. 21½″

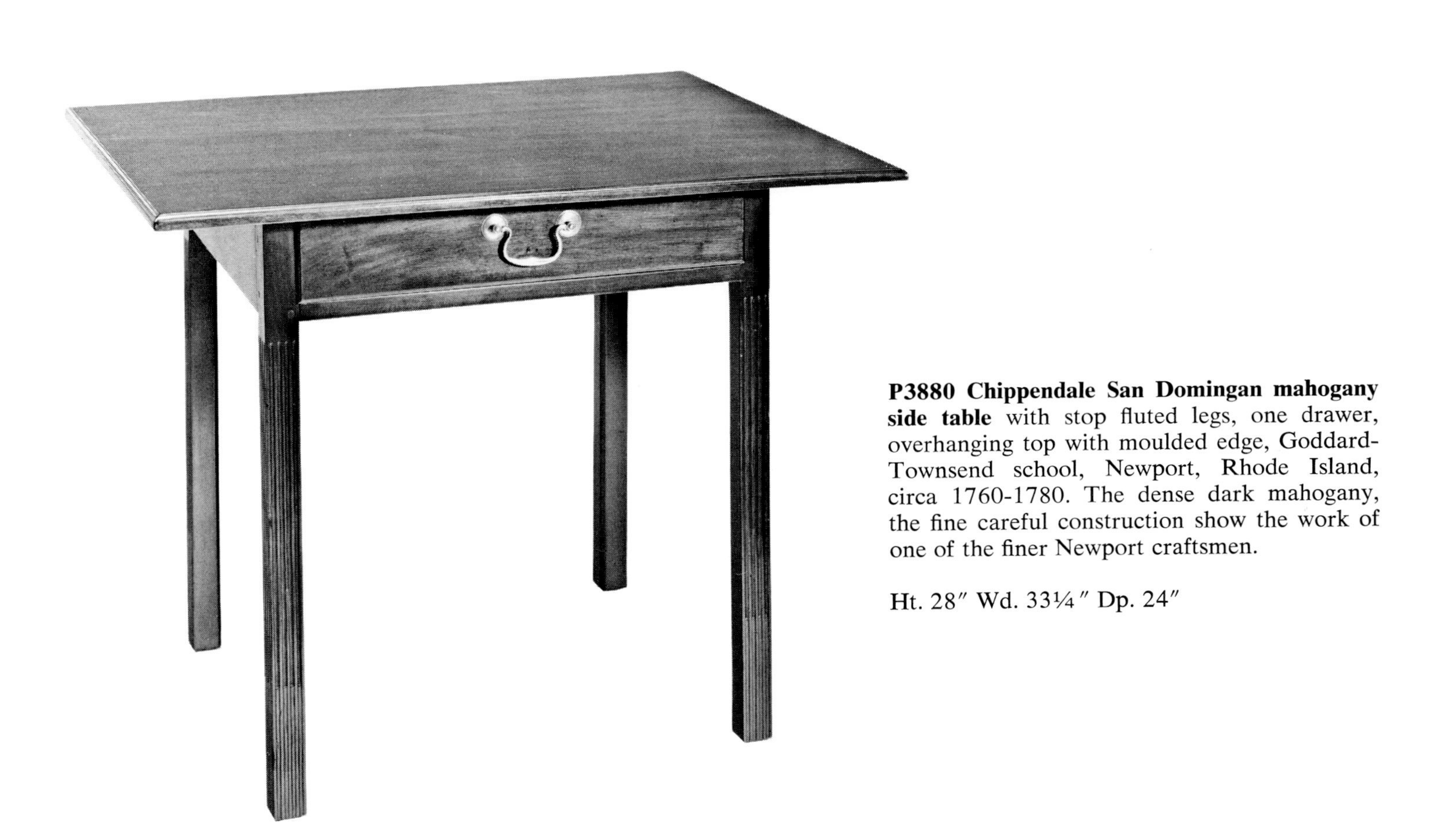

P3880 Chippendale San Domingan mahogany side table with stop fluted legs, one drawer, overhanging top with moulded edge, Goddard-Townsend school, Newport, Rhode Island, circa 1760-1780. The dense dark mahogany, the fine careful construction show the work of one of the finer Newport craftsmen.

Ht. 28″ Wd. 33¼″ Dp. 24″

P3869 Silver beaker with moulded rim and base, made and signed C. A. Burnett, Alexandria, Virginia, and Georgetown, D. C., circa 1790-1810. The contemporary monogram "M" is for the Magruder family of Maryland.

Ht. 3¼″ Dia. 2¾″

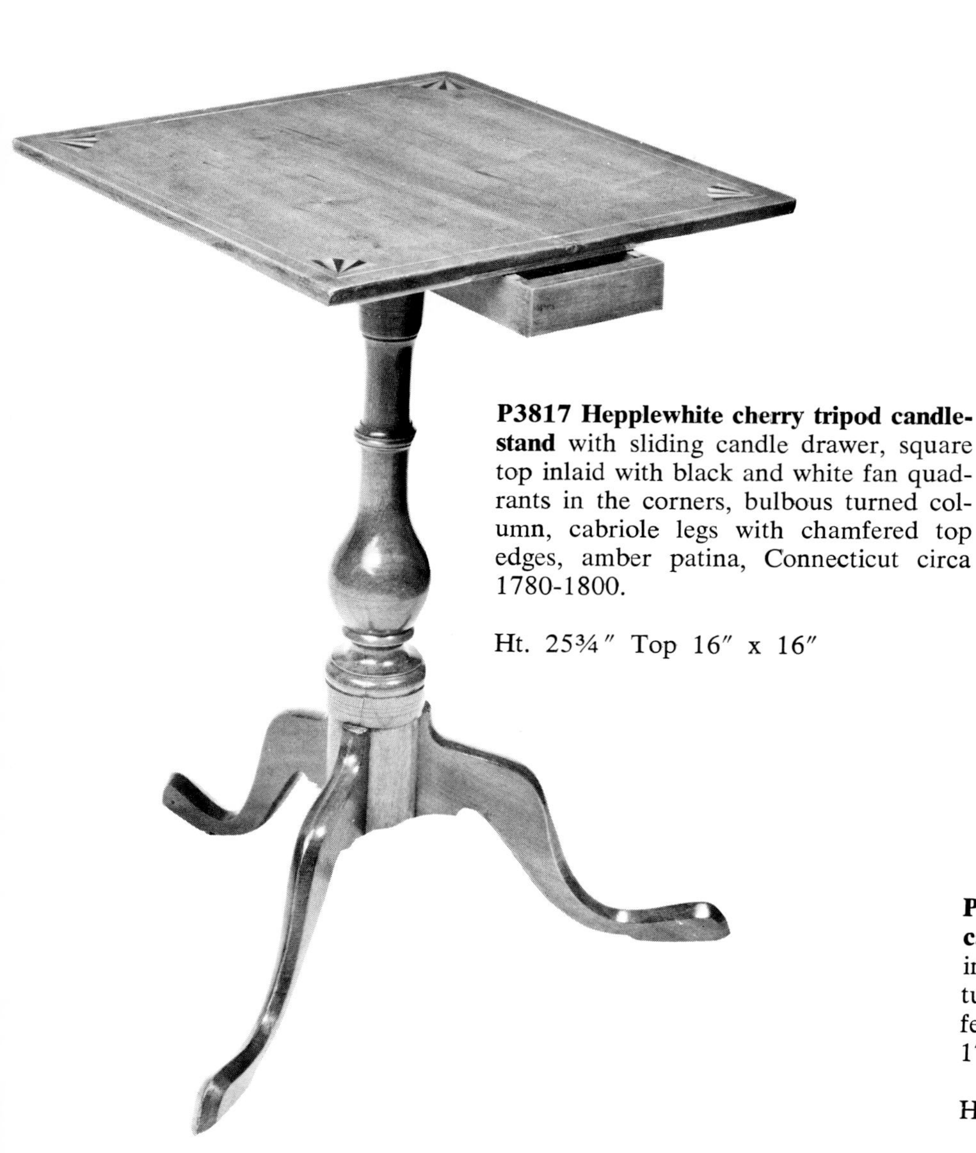

P3817 Hepplewhite cherry tripod candle-stand with sliding candle drawer, square top inlaid with black and white fan quadrants in the corners, bulbous turned column, cabriole legs with chamfered top edges, amber patina, Connecticut circa 1780-1800.

Ht. 25¾″ Top 16″ x 16″

P3777 Hepplewhite mahogany tripod tilt top candlestand, oval top with fine oval urn and floral inlaid center patera in green background, ring turned urn column, inlaid bowed legs with spade feet, mellow brown patina, Massachusetts circa 1780-1800.

Ht. 29″ Top 25⅜″ x 16⅜″

P3782 Hepplewhite cherry serpentine front bureau, curly maple veneered drawer fronts with crossbanded borders, conforming top with arrow inlaid border, outsplayed French feet, mellow patina, Massachusetts circa 1780-1800. Furnished with a superb set of eighteenth century brasses with eagle and shield and E. PLURIBUS UNUM.

Ht. 35¼″ Wd. 41″ Dp. 20″

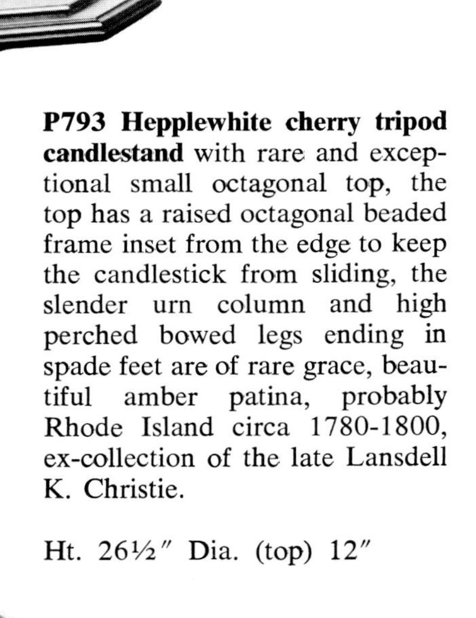

P793 Hepplewhite cherry tripod candlestand with rare and exceptional small octagonal top, the top has a raised octagonal beaded frame inset from the edge to keep the candlestick from sliding, the slender urn column and high perched bowed legs ending in spade feet are of rare grace, beautiful amber patina, probably Rhode Island circa 1780-1800, ex-collection of the late Lansdell K. Christie.

Ht. 26½″ Dia. (top) 12″

P3795 Sheraton mahogany armchair with graceful splat forming a strapwork lyre containing a carved urn, egg and dart crest panel, incurvate arms, tapered line inlaid legs, Philadelphia circa 1800-1810.

Ht. 36⅝″ Wd. 22¾″

P3826 Classical mahogany lyre alarm banjo clock, original eglomise glass panel with divided fluted center and scrolled and acanthus carved frame, bulged moulded base and acorn bracket, dial inscribed "Warranted by L. Curtis." The alarm mechanism is set by a numbered brass disc at the center of the dial which activates the exposed bell. Made by Lemuel Curtis, Concord, Massachusetts, circa 1820-1830.

Ht. 39″ Wd. 11″ Dp.5″

P3883 Bilbao mirror, black frame with beaded borders and gilt rosette corners, the festooned gilded top contains central motifs of arrows in a quiver, a crown and acanthus leaves, the base with conventional festooning, made in Bilbao, Spain, circa 1780-1800, bought by Captain Wormsted in Bilbao and brought to Marblehead, Massachusetts.

Ex-collection Francis Hill Bigelow. Illustrated Nutting "Furniture Treasury" Vol. II plate 2904.

Ht. 61″ W. 26″

P3889 Rare small size Hepplewhite mahogany serpentine front sideboard with sliding tray, the stiles and legs are fronted by curly satinwood panels, the center drawer contains an oval panel in curly satinwood or maple rectangle; the tapered legs are banded by raised line inlaid cuffs; beautiful mellow brown patina, Newport or Providence, Rhode Island, circa 1780-1800.

Ht. 40″ Wd. 54¾″ Dp. 22″

P3865 Pair of Classical mahogany lyre back side chairs, moulded saber legs, school of Duncan Phyfe, New York circa 1800-1815.

Ht. 32½″

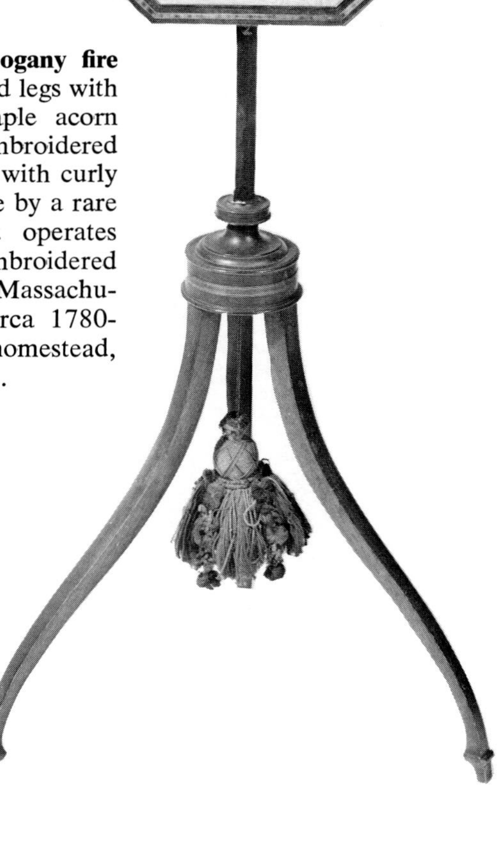

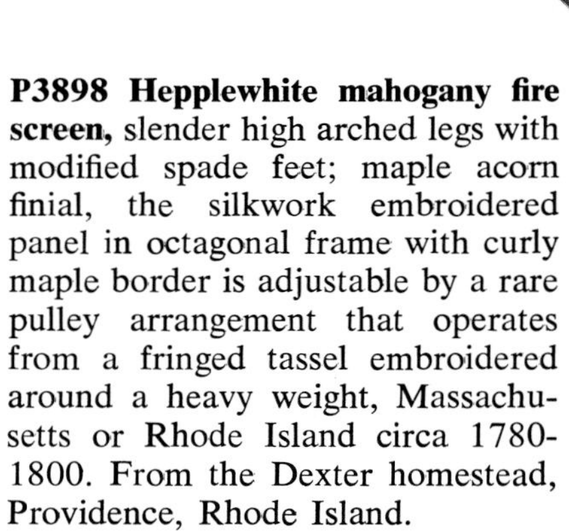

P3898 Hepplewhite mahogany fire screen, slender high arched legs with modified spade feet; maple acorn finial, the silkwork embroidered panel in octagonal frame with curly maple border is adjustable by a rare pulley arrangement that operates from a fringed tassel embroidered around a heavy weight, Massachusetts or Rhode Island circa 1780-1800. From the Dexter homestead, Providence, Rhode Island.

Ht. 56½″

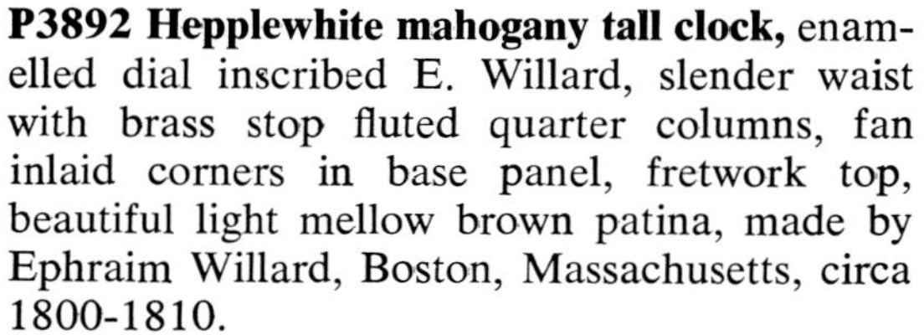

P3892 Hepplewhite mahogany tall clock, enamelled dial inscribed E. Willard, slender waist with brass stop fluted quarter columns, fan inlaid corners in base panel, fretwork top, beautiful light mellow brown patina, made by Ephraim Willard, Boston, Massachusetts, circa 1800-1810.

Ht. 7′7½″

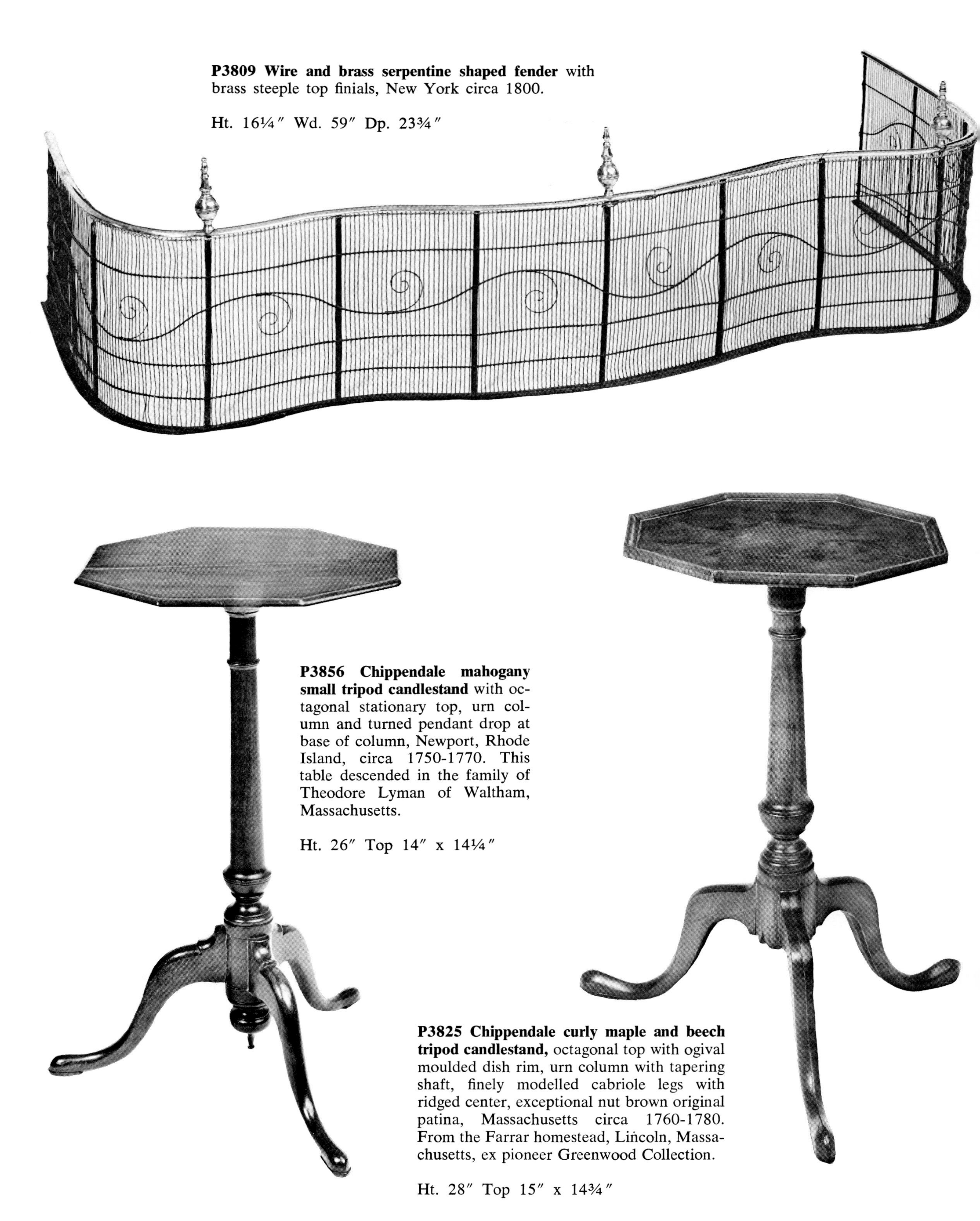

P3809 Wire and brass serpentine shaped fender with brass steeple top finials, New York circa 1800.

Ht. 16¼″ Wd. 59″ Dp. 23¾″

P3856 Chippendale mahogany small tripod candlestand with octagonal stationary top, urn column and turned pendant drop at base of column, Newport, Rhode Island, circa 1750-1770. This table descended in the family of Theodore Lyman of Waltham, Massachusetts.

Ht. 26″ Top 14″ x 14¼″

P3825 Chippendale curly maple and beech tripod candlestand, octagonal top with ogival moulded dish rim, urn column with tapering shaft, finely modelled cabriole legs with ridged center, exceptional nut brown original patina, Massachusetts circa 1760-1780. From the Farrar homestead, Lincoln, Massachusetts, ex pioneer Greenwood Collection.

Ht. 28″ Top 15″ x 14¾″

P3781 Sheraton mahogany sewing table, one drawer and sewing slide drawer with original spiral carved knobs, turret corners with ring turned capitals, the top is bordered by concentric ringed applied mouldings often associated with the shop of William Hook. Slender bulbous reeded legs, mellow brown patina, Salem, Massachusetts, circa 1800-1810.

Ht. 28¼″ Wd. 23¼″ Dp. 18¾″

P3864 Set of ten fancy Sheraton rush seat side chairs (two illustrated) retaining the original black and gilt decoration, the finely designed splats are formed of moulded black rings with gilt floral centers supported by stencilled lyres, New England circa 1810. These chairs descended in the family of Captain William Lord of Kennebunkport, Maine.

Ht. 33¼″

P3866 Pair of Hepplewhite mahogany shield back side chairs, drapery carved splats with plume and acanthus carved centers, tapered reeded legs ending in spade feet, New York circa 1780-1800. This is one of the finest New York Hepplewhite chair designs. The technique of the acanthus carving compares to that on classical forms by Duncan Phyfe.

Ht. 38½″

P3834. Hepplewhite cherry end table, two drawers with birdseye maple fronts, flanked by crotch veneered panels, tapered legs with line inlay, crested by fans, medial shelf with reeded borders, thin top with crossbanded top border, beautiful warm ruddy patina, Massachusetts circa 1790-1810.

Ht. 28″ Wd. 16″ Dp. 15¾″

P3835 Sheraton mahogany work table, rectangular case with two drawers flanked by reeded turret columns, the conforming top with reeded edge is hinged revealing writing compartment, delicate bulbous turned legs ending in brass casters, mellow light brown patina, New York circa 1800-1810.

Ht. 29½″ Wd. 20″ Dp. 15½″

P3706 Sheraton mahogany side chair, reeded slats with fan terminals, fluted rectangular panel in crest, reeded tapered legs ending in spade feet, school of Slover and Taylor, New York circa 1800-1810.

Ht. 35½″

P3798 Hepplewhite birch tripod candlestand, oval tilt top, finely turned urn and bulbous column, ridged platformed pad feet, medium brown color, Massachusetts circa 1770-1790.

Ht. 28¼″ Top 22¾″ x 14¼″

P3824 Hepplewhite mahogany pembroke table, oval top with drop leaves and concave moulded edges, drawer in one end, line inlaid tapering legs with cuffs, New York circa 1780-1800. From the Remsen Family of Brooklyn.

Ht. 28½″ Lg. 32″ Wd. open 42″ closed 20¾″

P3903 & B Hepplewhite console table with original white and grey striated marble top, the rectangular base with tapered legs is maple and pine with original grained surface to simulate figured veneer, the graining is highlighted by a silvered dotted drapery and line borders; the marble top is a beautiful cyma shaped outline with finely moulded edge. Portsmouth, New Hampshire circa 1780-1800.

Ht. 33½″ Wd. 40½″ Dp. 17¾″

P3893 Classical mahogany card table; the finely figured veneered top swivels revealing a box compartment in the rounded corner case; the case is supported on two tapering octagonal panelled columns connected by octagonal panelled cross stretcher; acanthus carved and moulded legs with brass casters, superb quality and color, attributed to Dunçan Phyfe, New York, circa 1820. This table descended in the same family and is related in detail as the labelled Phyfe secretary in "Duncan Phyfe" Nancy McClelland, plate 251. It is also related to the card table made by Duncan Phyfe for John Jacob Astor, McClelland plate 239.

Ht. 29½″ Wd. 36″ Dp. 18″

P3863 Pair of Sheraton mahogany side chairs, drapery carved splats supported by acanthus carved upright slats, egg and dart carved crest panels, moulded tapered legs, Philadelphia circa 1800-1810.

Ht. 35″

A FROTHINGHAM MASTERPIECE

P3741 Chippendale mahogany blockfront chest-on-chest; the lower case with square blocking capped with rounded corners, bracket feet with blocked inner outline, the upper case with drawers flanked by fluted columns, the upper row with center drawer featuring a complex shell and acanthus carved motif in punchwork background (see detail) flanked by end drawers that follow the outline of the arch; the original open flame finials with acanthus carved bowls, choice golden patina, original brasses, attributed to Benjamin Frothingham, Charlestown, Massachusetts, circa 1760-1780.
The characteristics that relate to labelled Frothingham examples are evidenced in the distinctive carved shell and open flame finials that appear on a blockfront chest-on-chest labelled by Benjamin Frothingham illustrated in ANTIQUES magazine November 1952 Frontispiece.

Ht. 7′9¾″ Wd. 41¾″ Dp. 21½″

FULL CIRCLE

Since our firm was founded in 1903, there have been cycles of collecting which seem to span a twenty to thirty year period. The collections our firm was instrumental in putting together in the early 1900's were in a great many instances dispersed in whole or in part in the 1920's. The collections formed in the 1920's were offered in the 30's and 40's, and the great wave of collecting in the 30's and 40's came to market in the 60's and in some cases in our present decade.

At each turn of the wheel we have always been and will continue to be available to catch the choice examples offered. Our tremendous activity over the past seven decades puts in a position to be a dominant source. While the higher prices and growing scarcity encourages counterfeiting and traps the unwary or naive, our main thrust has been and will be to sort out for the ever growing group of new collectors the best that has been the nucleus of this elite circle.

However, at each turn of the wheel, one must remember, that some pieces are not offered and possibly never will be, either remaining as family possessions or as gifts to institutions. So as the wheel spins the fall-out becomes smaller and the rarity increases.

Mr. Israel Sack was the main guiding light and source for the famous collection of the late Mitchel Taradash. Some of these choice pieces were offered to us and we recently purchased them. We now take great pleasure in giving you—the new fortunate group of current collectors—the opportunity to participate in this cycle of connoisseurship.

HAROLD SACK   ALBERT M. SACK   ROBERT M. SACK

THE WHITTIER CHEST

P3939 Pilgrim oak, maple and pine "Hadley" chest retaining the original red and black decoration, the center panel of the three panelled front bears the initials HM with an inverted heart above; the simple chamfered borders to the panels indicate placement of this chest in the earlier group, the original pine top is hinged by cotter pins in their original setting; two drawers below; the framed sides contain four panels; the front of the chest containing the typical Hadley carved decoration is entirely of maple, made in the vicinity of Hadley, Massachusetts, circa 1690-1710, and in the finest original state of preservation. This chest is listed in Luther "Hadley Chest" #48. Illustrated "Fine Points of Furniture, Early American," page 109.

Ex Collection Albert Whittier, Beverly, Massachusetts.

Ht. 40½″ Wd. 44″ Dp. 17¾″

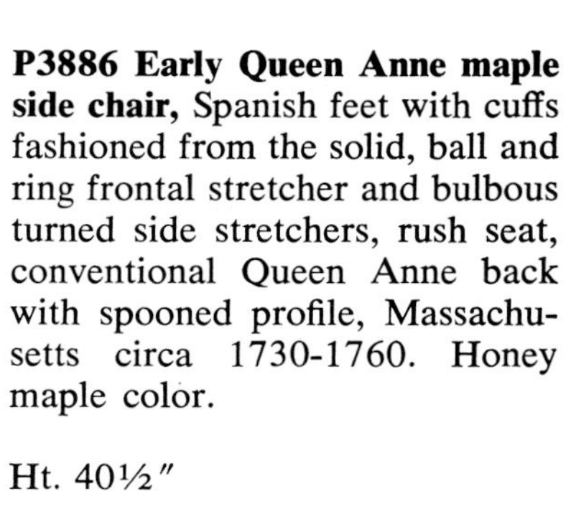

P3886 Early Queen Anne maple side chair, Spanish feet with cuffs fashioned from the solid, ball and ring frontal stretcher and bulbous turned side stretchers, rush seat, conventional Queen Anne back with spooned profile, Massachusetts circa 1730-1760. Honey maple color.

Ht. 40½″

P3957 Early maple and curly maple oval top tavern table of rare small size; the bulbous turned legs rake in both directions and the ball feet are intact; the table has been refinished some years ago and has a pleasing honey color, Massachusetts circa 1710-1730.

Ht. 23½″ Top 26½″ x 21″

P3887 Early Queen Anne maple side chair, Spanish feet with cuffs fashioned from the solid, ball and ring frontal stretcher, rush seat, conventional Queen Anne back with spooned profile, Massachusetts circa 1730-1760. Honey maple color.

Ht. 40½″

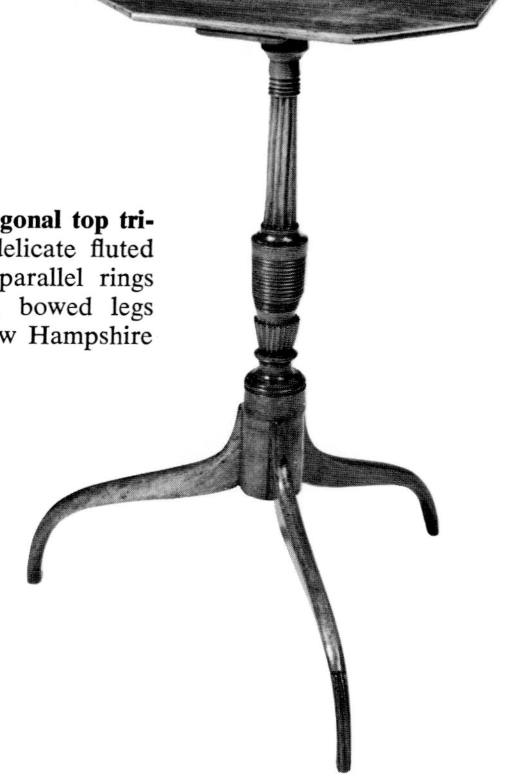

P3909 Hepplewhite birch octagonal top tripod candlestand, interesting delicate fluted column with large urn with parallel rings above a smaller reeded urn, bowed legs with reeded panel at base, New Hampshire circa 1800-1810.

Ht. 28″ Top 15¾″ × 12¾″

P3953 Unique set of seven early Queen Anne chairs consisting of one arm and six side chairs, the chairs are of the familiar North Shore design but are more carefully modelled than most; the Spanish feet with scrolled platform are fashioned from the solid; the side and rear stretchers are bulbous turned, rush seats, the finely spooned Queen Anne backs have moulded stiles and crests with horned yoke centers, the armchair has finely moulded serpentine arms with scrolled terminals, the chairs are in superb orginal state retaining the original brown painted surfaces; Salem, Massachusetts, circa 1730-1740.

This set of chairs were purchased by Israel Sack at an auction sale of the effects of the Gay Homestead in Suffield, Connecticut, in 1915. The set was sold by Israel Sack to Albert Whittier in 1915. An interior of the Gay Homestead showing the chairs prior to 1915 is illustrated in "Suffield Furniture" by Charles Bissell, see illustration. We have recently repurchased this set from the Whittier family for approximately fifty times the original cost to Albert Whittier in 1915.

Armchair: Ht. 43½″ Wd. 23″

Side chairs: Ht. 42½″

PLATE 53—THE GAY MANSION, C. 1795

P4010 Chippendale birch octagonal or pencil post bed, slender tapering head and foot posts of full length retaining the old red paint, original rails and original pine headboard, flat tester, Massachusetts circa 1740-1760.

Ht. 69¾″ Wd. 51⅜″ Ln. 75¼″

P3998 Early maple and curly maple five slat back armchair, the slats with deeply bowed profile, fine ball and ring turned frontal stretcher and ball feet intact, mellow amber color, Pennsylvania circa 1720-1750.

Ht. 47½″ Wd. 23½″

P4004 Chippendale cherry standing slant top desk in two sections, the lower section with plinth base and four graduated drawers, the slant top section with one drawer; fine serpentine blocked interior, the center section is one tall drawer with concave blocked and fan carved front, Connecticut circa 1770-1790. To our knowledge this form is rare or unique.

Ht. 46″ Wd. 28″ Dp. 17″

P3915 Hepplewhite birch and birdseye maple end table, the table has two drawers with birdseye fronts and banded borders, the lower drawer fronting a compartment with ring pierced gallery, original chased brass knobs, New Hampshire circa 1800-1810.

Ht. 28¾″ Wd. 20″ Dp. 16¾″

P4012 Silver bowl with footed base, base and top edge with gadrooned border, bearing the contemporary monogram "L," marked Churchill, made by Lemuel Churchill, Boston, Massachusetts, circa 1800.

Ht. 4″ Dia. 6¾″

P3997 Chippendale mahogany corner chair, frontal cabriole leg with acanthus carved knee, ball and claw foot with swept back talons, side and rear legs tapering with cylindrical platformed feet, interlaced splats with scrolled volutes flanked by fluted columns, finely shaped arm rests, beautiful golden color, Boston, Massachusetts, circa 1760-1780. This chair is virtually identical to one in "Fine Points of Furniture, Early American," page 74.

Ht. 31¼″ Wd. 31″

P3950 Chippendale mahogany tripod bird-cage dishtop candlestand, one piece top with crisply moulded dish rim, finely turned ball and ring turned column, platformed pad feet, Philadelphia circa 1750-1780. The table is fashioned of close grained mahogany with a fine old patina.

Ht. 29″ Dia. 19″

P3990 Pair of Chippendale mahogany claw and ball foot side chairs of tall stately proportion, acanthus carved knees and knee returns, the latter ending in scrolled volutes, convex shell centering aprons, interlaced splats with scrolled volutes, serpentine crests with cabachon carved centers and moulded scrolled ears, fluted stiles, fine old finish, Philadelphia circa 1760-1780.

Ht. 41¼″

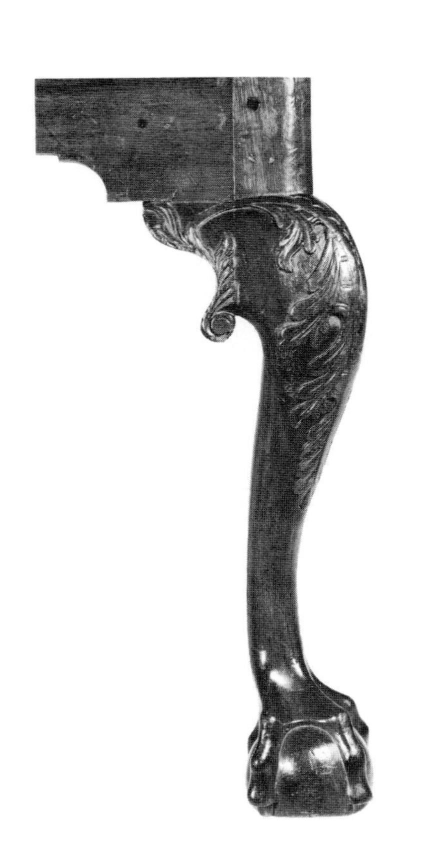

P3958 Queen Anne walnut mirror, scrolled crest and base, carved and gilded three plumed motif silhouetted in crest, original bevelled mirror in carved and gilded border, English circa 1740-1760.

Ht. 35″ Wd. 19″

P3973 Rare diminutive Queen Anne San Domingan mahogany whist table, turret ends and turreted knee returns with cyma scrolled outline, platformed wafer pad feet, felt lined interior surface with candle pockets and scoops, Boston, Massachusetts, circa 1740-1760. This table relates in form to a group of Boston tables with turreted knees.

1. Oliver Wendell Holmes card table, Sack brochure #16, #1195.
2. Turreted card table, Randall, "American Furniture," #7.
3. Turreted tea table, Museum of Fine Arts, Boston, Karolik #60.
4. Turreted tea table, Henry Francis du Pont Winterthur Museum, Downs #370.

The impact of the diminutive size and brilliant modelling of this little gem has to be seen to be believed. Fortunately it retains its original unstained maple and pine structure and glue blocks.

Ht. 27¼″ Wd. 25¾″ Dp. 13¼

P3949 Chippendale mahogany tripod birdcage dish top candlestand, bulbous and ring turned column, pad feet, light brown color, Philadelphia circa 1750-1780. The table is of convenient low height.

Ht. 26½″ Dia. 23¾″

P3964 Chippendale San Domingan mahogany Martha Washington armchair or "lolling" chair, the arm supports with the flaring scrolled base and the serpentine arms with lobed terminals are typical of a group of small scale upholstered armchairs often attributed to Joseph Short, square legs with beaded edges, serpentine crest. The chair is fashioned of close grained mahogany with a fine bronze patina, Newburyport, Massachusetts, circa 1760-1780.

Ht. 44″ Wd. 27″

P3952 Sheraton mahogany sofa with incurvate reeded arms, three panel ribbon and sheaf of wheat carved back, reeded seat frame and reeded legs ending in brass casters, choice mellow brown patina, made by Duncan Phyfe or a contemporary, New York circa 1800-1810. Sold by Israel Sack thirty years ago and recently repurchased.

Ht. 36½″ Lg. 6′ 8″ Dp. 25½″

P3963 Sheraton gilded mirror with spiral columns, the exceptional eglomise glass panel depicts a naval engagement in the War of 1812. The painting (which has a crack running through the water area) is contained in an oval, the lower spandrels with banners reading "BATTLE ON LAKE ERIE", Massachusetts circa 1815-1825.

Ht. 42″ Wd. 28″

PETER G[illegible]N.
Main-street, PROVIDENCE, [illegible]
OFFER FOR [illegible]ALE,
A COMP[illegible]TE assortment of PAINTS, [illegible]
VARNISHES, and
SHIP-CHANDLERY...
ALSO
Looking-Glasses,
[illegible] in the [illegible] and most elegant style, and are warranted to bear the strictest examination......With every [illegible] article usually called for in a Ship-Chandlery or Paint Store, as cheap as [illegible] store in the State.
They execute all kinds of
HOUSE, SHIP, SIGN and ORNAMENTAL PAINTING,
polishing and re-silvering old Looking Glasses, Oil and Burnish Gilding, in all their various branches. [illegible] Looking-Glasses and Pictures of every description, framed with enamelled glasses, as usual.
All orders from the country punctually attended to, with a liberal allowance made to those who purchase quantities.
PRINTED AT THE PHENIX OFFICE.

P3985 Sheraton gilt mirror with original eglomise glass panel depicting a landscape in pastel colors with gilt scrolled border and white background, the frame with spiral gilt borders, the mirror bears the original label of Peter Grinnell, Main Street, Providence, circa 1800-1810.

Ht. 37½″ Wd. 20″

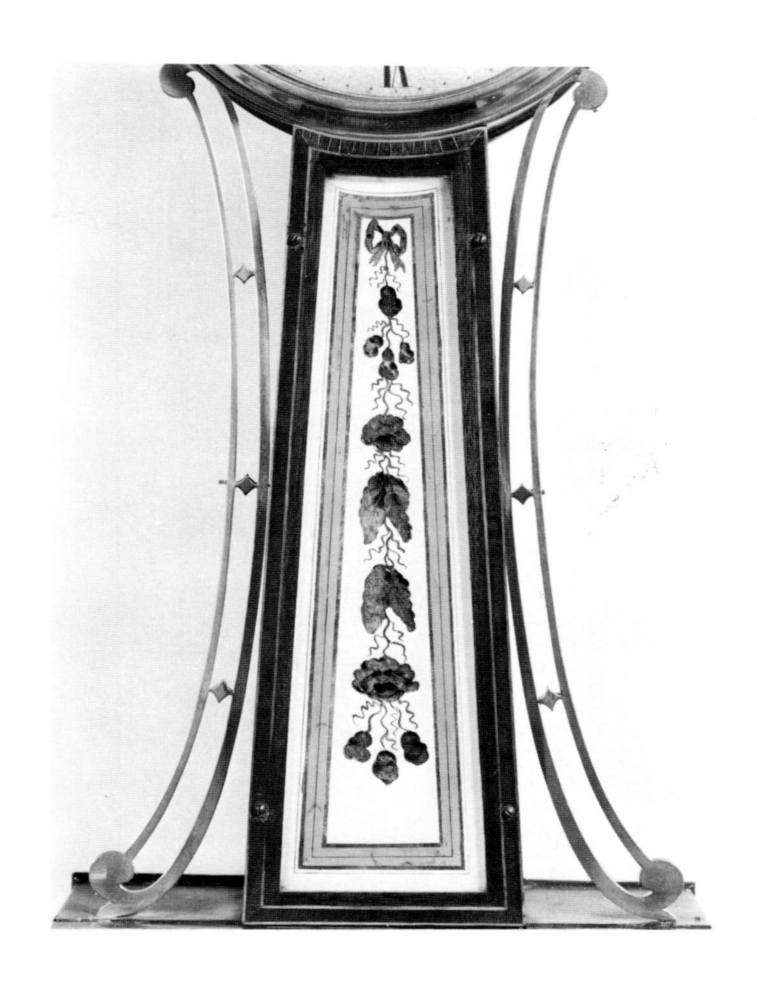

P3978 Mahogany and gilt banjo clock with the original eglomise glass waist and door panels, the door panel inscribed "S. Willard's Patent." The door panel is composed of a crescent with bellflower spandrels in powder blue inner and outer borders on white background, the waist panel is composed of flowers and vines in a powder blue border on white background; both panels are contained in frames with crossbanded borders, the waist panel secured by four screws; the base bracket retains the original gilt, the brass eagle is the original as are the works which have the T-bridge escapement mechanism. This clock is in the finest original state, made by Simon Willard, Roxbury, Massachusetts, circa 1802-1815. Ex Collection the late Mitchel Taradash. Illustrated ANTIQUES January 1953, page 44 and "Living with Antiques" Alice Winchester, page 91.

Ht. 43″ Wd. 10″ Dp. 3½″

P3928 Pair of Sheraton mahogany side chairs, the center splats are in the shape of a solid urn with drapery, acanthus and fluted carving with fleur de lis terminal, tapered legs, Philadelphia circa 1800-1810. A chair of this design is illustrated in "Federal Furniture" Charles F. Montgomery plate 98.

Ht. 36″

P3938 Pair of Sheraton mahogany side chairs, the crest panel with carved vines emanating from looped center, the splat formed of two opposing moulded arches with medallion carved center, bowed seats with reeded frames, reeded legs ending in bulbous feet, rich bronze color, attributed to Duncan Phyfe, New York circa 1800-1810. The panel design is shown in Cornelius "Masterpieces of Duncan Phyfe" plate #8.

Ht. 32″

P3972 Sheraton mahogany sewing table, rectangular top with canted corners; the top is bordered by parallel rings, turret corners with star punch top surface and fluted sides, the reeded legs have egg and dart carved border, the water leaf carved capitals have star punched background, the case has one fitted top drawer and a sewing drawer, mellow bronze patina, attributed to William Hook, Salem, Massachusetts, circa 1800-1810. The attribution to William Hook is based on the relationship of the ring turned top edge and the technique of the carved capitals with the same motifs on the pieces made in 1809 by William Hook for his sister, now in the Museum of Fine Arts, Boston. See Randall, #99. Also see ANTIQUES page 144, 1934 April for the detail of the capital of the documented Hook table.

Ht. 28¾″ Top 21″ x 16¼″

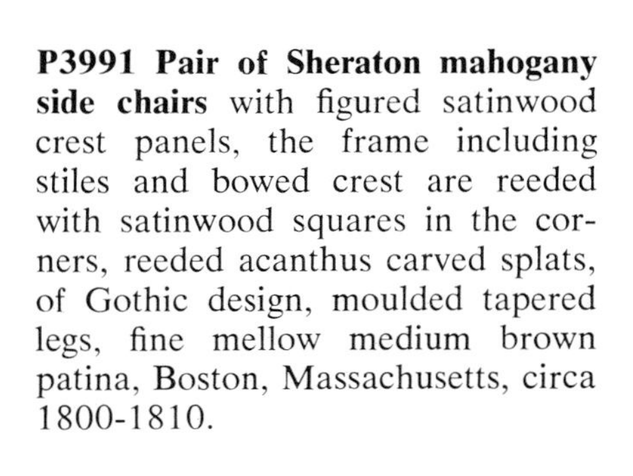

P3991 Pair of Sheraton mahogany side chairs with figured satinwood crest panels, the frame including stiles and bowed crest are reeded with satinwood squares in the corners, reeded acanthus carved splats, of Gothic design, moulded tapered legs, fine mellow medium brown patina, Boston, Massachusetts, circa 1800-1810.

Ht. 35¾″

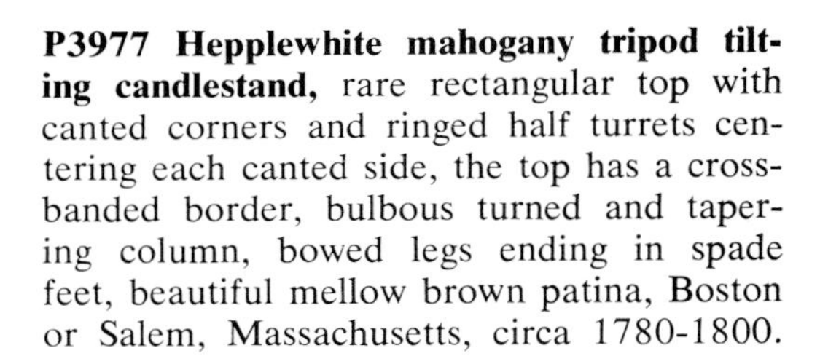

P3977 Hepplewhite mahogany tripod tilting candlestand, rare rectangular top with canted corners and ringed half turrets centering each canted side, the top has a crossbanded border, bulbous turned and tapering column, bowed legs ending in spade feet, beautiful mellow brown patina, Boston or Salem, Massachusetts, circa 1780-1800.

Ht. 28⅜″ Top 21″ x 14½″

P3930 Hepplewhite mahogany small secretary-desk, three drawers in lower case with fine figured grain and crossbanded borders, tapered bellflower inlaid legs and inlaid cuffs; the stiles have tooth inlaid border, the inlay continuing on the fronts of the narrow pullout slides; the glass doors of the upper case form four evenly spaced arches supported by inlaid pilasters, the doors enclose small drawers and pigeonholes, fine golden patina, Massachusetts circa 1790-1800.

Ht. 52¾″ Wd. 38″ Dp. 19½″

Wrtg. Lvl. 33½″

P850 Sheraton mahogany armchair, the drapery and plume splat design is usually associated with New York examples, the splat of this rare Massachusetts example has fluted and notched facades, serpentine arms, tapered moulded legs, stretchers, attractive light nut brown patina, Massachusetts circa 1800-1810.

Ht. 36″ Wd. 20¾″

P3902 Rare stumpwork embroidered panel depicting a coronation scene, in original black and gilt frame, fine state of preservation, English 17th century.

Ht. 19½″ Wd. 25½″

P3906 Sheraton mahogany armchair, three moulded splats with acanthus carving, the center splat arrow shaped, fluted crest panel, serpentine arms and arm supports, moulded tapered legs, stretchers, Massachusetts circa 1800-1810.

Ht. 36″ Wd. 22″

P3971 Sheraton mahogany and flame satinwood sewing table, rectangular shaped case with turret ends, the case containing two drawers in front and sewing slide at side, the drawer fronts, turret corners and twin panelled sides have beautifully figured flame satinwood veneer with crossbanded and inlaid borders, the edge bordered by lunette inlay; the conforming top is veneered with a burl center panel, with curly maple and blistered exotic wood and inlaid borders, the exquisitely delicate tapering reeded legs with bulbous and ring turned capitals are typical of a group of related tables by John Seymour; the richly patterned veneered top is also typical of this group (see Stoneman #138 and #139A). The mellow original patina of the table is superb, serving to blend the various veneered patterns into a harmonious unit. Attributed to John Seymour, Boston, Massachusetts circa 1800-1810. Ex Collection, the late Mitchel Taradash, illustrated ANTIQUES June 1946, page 360.

Ht. 30″ Top 21¼″ x 17″

P3910 Queen Anne maple side chair, upholstered back and seat, moulded spooned stiles and moulded arched crest, squared cabriole legs with scribed borders ending in Spanish feet, ball and ring turned frontal stretcher, North Shore, Massachusetts, or New Hampshire circa 1740-1750.

Ht. 42″

P3937 Queen Anne walnut side chair, the seat and knees with shell carving, the cabriole legs with scrolled knee returns and platformed disc feet, vase shaped veneered splat and serpentine crest with cabachon carved center and rolled ears, attributed to John Elliott, Philadelphia circa 1750-1760.

The base of this chair is identical to that of the set of four Elliott stools in the Henry F. du Pont Winterthur Museum, illustrated Downs "American Furniture" pl. 294.

Ht. 40″

P3931 Queen Anne walnut and maple side chair of tall slender proportion, straight seat with scalloped apron, cyma and crescent shaped flat medial stretcher joined by block and arrow turned side stretchers, slender cabriole legs, Newport, Rhode Island, circa 1740-1760.

Ht. 41⅝″

P3960 Small Chippendale mahogany mirror with scrolled crest and base, finely sculptured gilt Phoenix silhouetted in crest, original glass and back, American or English circa 1760-1780.

Ht. 26¾″ Wd. 15½″

P3929 Chippendale curly maple high chest of drawers, the case with six rows of graduated drawers, the top row simulating three with the center featuring a carved fan, bracket feet with spurred inner outline, chestnut lined throughout, original warm amber patina, Rhode Island circa 1760-1780.

Ht. 48½″ Wd. 36″ Dp. 18¾″

P4000 Set of four Chippendale mahogany side chairs, assymetrical acanthus carved knees, hairy paw claw and ball feet with swept back talons, solid pierced splats with carved diamond centers and acanthus borders, stop fluted stiles, acanthus carved ears, Boston, Massachusetts, circa 1760-1770. A chair of this set was shown in the Metropolitan Museum Exhibit "American Art from American Collections" 1963, catalogue #14. The distinctive knee carving is seen on a number of Boston pieces such as the settees in the Metropolitan Museum and Henry F. du Pont Winterthur Museum—see Downs #270. This carving and hairy paw foot can be seen on the Boston chair in Downs #151.

This set of chairs descended in the Marquand family of Boston and Newburyport. They were purchased by us from a direct descendant.

Ht. 37½″

P3024 Pair of Hepplewhite mahogany five legged demi-lune card tables, the tops have sunburst inlaid centers and crossbanded borders on mottled veneered background, the frames with crossbanded panels with fan inlaid corners, the tapered legs are inlaid with delicate bellflowers and pellets bordered by loops, the plinths above contain oval picture with lilies of the valley in dark green or black background, beautiful golden brown patina, attributed to William Whitehead, New York circa 1780-1800. Descended in the Green family of Newport. The attribution to William Whitehead is based on the relationship of the distinctive looped bellflower inlay to that on two superb New York sideboards bearing the Whitehead label. Cf. (1) labelled Whitehead sideboard, Sack brochure #18, #1449 and (2) Robert Fulton sideboard labelled Whitehead, Lewis sale 1961, catalogue #259.

Ht. 29″ Wd. 35″ Dp. 17½″

P3980 Hepplewhite mahogany and gilt mirror, retains the original gilded fluted urn ornament with floral sprays and original side leaves, broken arch top ending in carved rosettes, carved and gilded inner and outer mirror borders, mellow brown patina, New York circa 1780-1800.

Ht. 46″ Wd. 19″

P3907 Federal mahogany serpentine front bureau retaining the Chippendale form, the serpentine outline flows to pointed ends, the line of the pointed ends continues through the ogee bracket feet, the drawer fronts are a finely figured crotch veneer with line inlaid and beaded borders, original bold chased oval brasses, Massachusetts circa 1780-1790.

Ht. 34½″ Wd. 39¾″ Dp. 22½″

P3969 Chippendale mahogany octagonal top tripod candle-stand, the top is fashioned of superbly figured solid crotch mahogany; the edge is bordered by applied fluting with a cup slide at one end; the column is formed of a spiral fluted urn with tapered fluting above; the cabriole legs with C-scrolled marginal inner borders; platformed pad feet; a ridge runs from the point of each foot along the leg surface ending in a leaf carved motif; the table is in an exceptional state of preservation; care and much polishing have given an exciting glow to the finely figured top; attributed to John Townsend, Newport, Rhode Island, circa 1760-1780. In our opinion this is the finest and highest developed Newport candlestand in any public or private collection.

This table originally belonged to Dr. David Townsend, a surgeon who was with General Warren in the Battle of Bunker Hill. Descended to Lillian Townsend Wade.

Ex-collection the late Mitchel Taradash.

Illustrated "Arts and Crafts of Newport" Carpenter #53.

Ht. 28½" Top 23½" x 16¼"

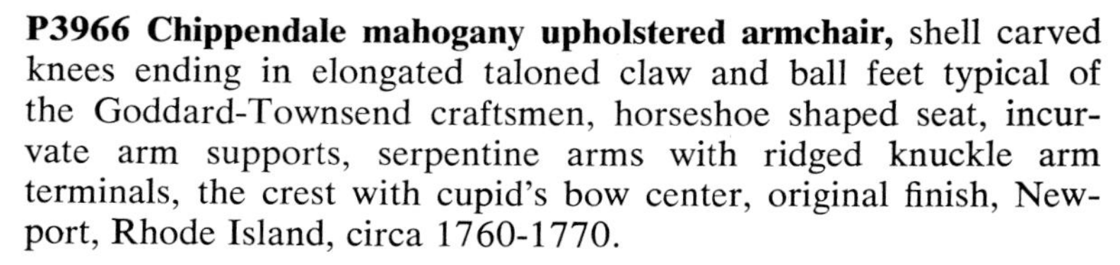

P3966 Chippendale mahogany upholstered armchair, shell carved knees ending in elongated taloned claw and ball feet typical of the Goddard-Townsend craftsmen, horseshoe shaped seat, incurvate arm supports, serpentine arms with ridged knuckle arm terminals, the crest with cupid's bow center, original finish, Newport, Rhode Island, circa 1760-1770.

Ex-Collection Dwight Blaney, pioneer collector.

Illustrated "Colonial Furniture in America" by Luke Vincent Lockwood, Volume II, Figure 582.

Illustrated "Arts and Crafts of Newport," by Ralph C. Carpenter, Jr., plate 25.

Ex-Collection the late Mitchel Taradash.

Ht. 43½" Wd. 29½" Dp. 26¾"

THE WHARTON CHAIRS

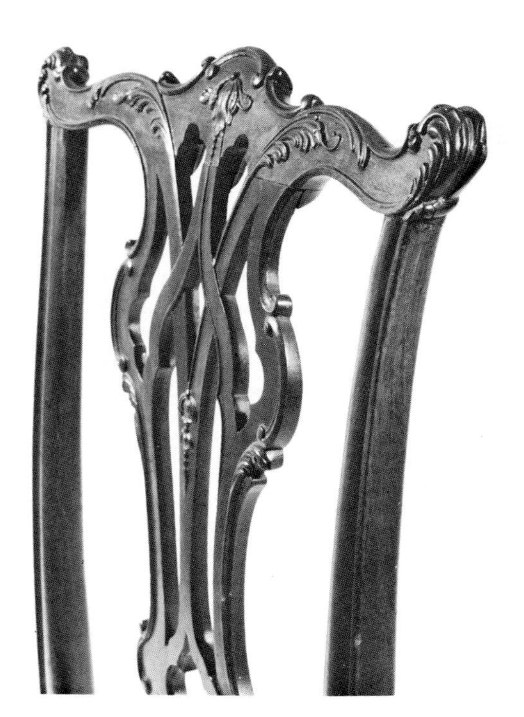

Parlor at 336 Spruce St Phil.
where [illegible] mother Wharton
lived for [illegible] years.
J.S.L. Wharton

P4011 Pair of Chippendale mahogany claw and ball foot side chairs; the chairs are of the highest order with gothic splat bordered by marginal carving, the crest rail superbly carved with floral center and acanthus ending in carved ears of three dimensional effect; the apron is cyma shaped with incised scrolled border, acanthus carved knees with inner marginal borders; the chairs are in the finest original state retaining the original reinforcing blocks and hard pine seat frames. Philadelphia circa 1760-1780. This pair of chairs is part of a set of at least twelve chairs made for Thomas Wharton or Charles Wharton of Philadelphia. These chairs were purchased by us directly from the Wharton family with considerable documentation, both in supporting family records and inscriptions on the chairs. The chairs stood in the house of Charles W. Wharton on Second Street above Spruce Street. The old photograph shows the chairs in the parlor at 336 Spruce Street, Philadelphia. The chairs, or chairs of the set, are shown in Hornor's "Blue Book of Philadelphia Furniture" plate 362. Hornor notes that Thomas Affleck is known to have made furniture for Thomas Wharton and suggests Affleck as the maker of the chairs.

Ht. 38½″

P3967 Queen Anne walnut corner chair, four cabriole legs, claw and ball feet with high ridged knuckles in the early manner, balloon seat, solid violin splats, original finish and condition, Newport, Rhode Island, circa 1740-1760.

Ex-Collection the late Mitchel Taradash

Illustrated ANTIQUES June 1946 page 358.

Ht. 31″ Wd. 28½″

P3917 Sheraton mahogany serpentine shaped sideboard of rare small size, the center is bowed with one drawer over cupboard doors, a sliding tray is over the drawer; the ends are concave with one drawer and deep cupboard in each section; the sections are divided by reeded turrets with ring turned capitals, the turrets are supported on bulbous reeded legs with bulbous turnings above and below, the top is bordered by parallel rings, a motif often associated with the work of William Hook, fine nut brown patina, Salem, Massachusetts, circa 1800-1810.

Ht. 40″ Wd. 58½″ Dp. 22½″

P3955 Sheraton "Bilbao" mirror, marble columns Corinthian capitals, festooned crest and base, imported for the American market, circa 1790-1810.

Ht. 41″ Wd. 19″

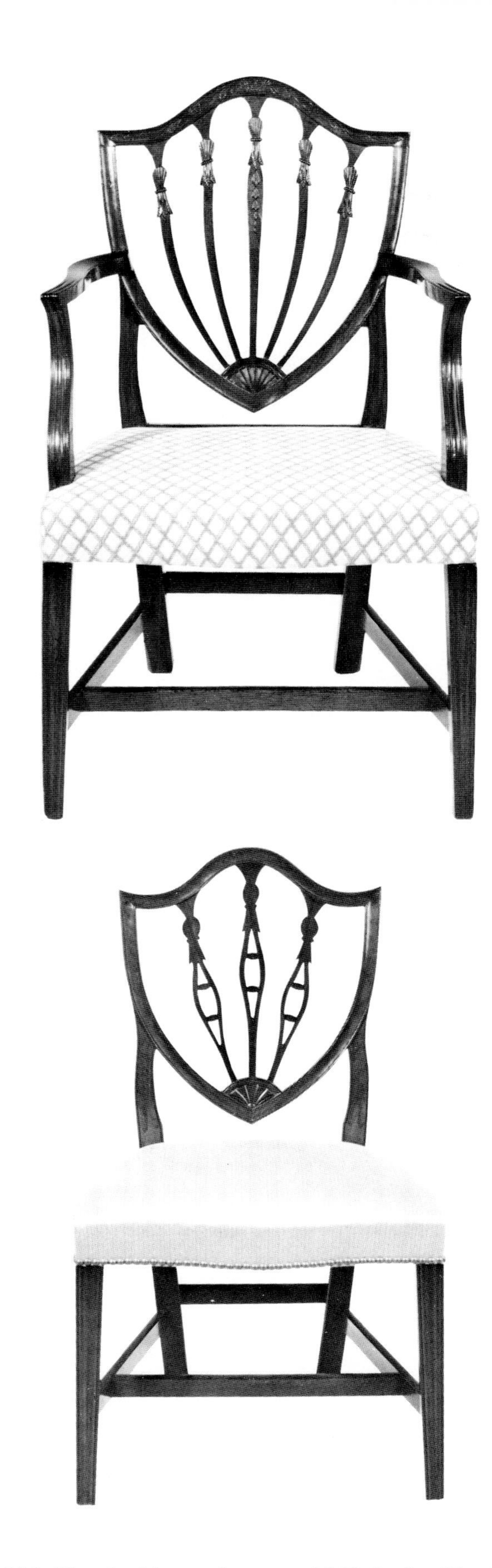

P3989 Hepplewhite mahogany shield back armchair, the boldly shaped shield crest carved with basket of fruit center motif with vine, leaf and acorn carving extending to the peaked ends, the splat with five slats with sheaf of wheat carved members, the center slat with bellflower carving emanating from fan inlaid base, incurvate shaped arms with moulded arm supports and moulded tapered legs, carving school of Samuel McIntire, Salem, Massachusetts, circa 1780-1800.

History: Descended in the Allyn family of Wellesley, Massachusetts.

Ht. 39½″ Wd. 24″

P3956 Hepplewhite mahogany shield back side chair, the three splats in the back are an interesting variation with silhouetted discs contained in ovals; the distinctive shape of the shield and the tassel outline of the splats relate to the labelled Jacob Forster side chair (Montgomery "Federal Furniture" plate 32); Boston or Charlestown, Massachusetts, circa 1790-1800.

Ht. 37½″

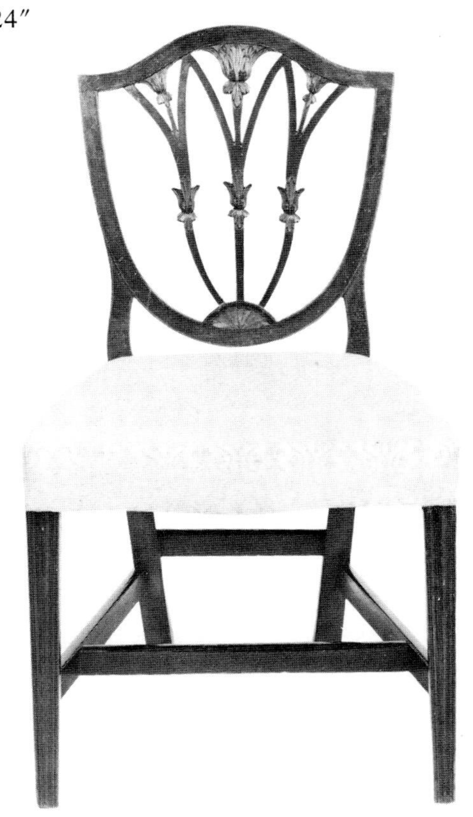

P3927 Hepplewhite mahogany shield back side chair, three slats centered by carved flowers and flaring to carved tulips with stippled background, tapered moulded legs, Salem, Massachusetts, circa 1780-1800.

Ht. 36½″

THE RUTGERS SOFA

P3926 Hepplewhite mahogany camel back sofa, sweeping serpentine curved back and seat with flaring rolled arms, line inlaid tapered legs ending in spade feet hewn from the solid with a mellow brown patina, H stretchers, New York circa 1780-1790. Descended in the family of Henry Rutgers, founder of Rutgers University.

Ht. 40″ Wd. 7′ 9¼″ Dp. 38″

P3943 Chippendale mahogany lowboy, fan carved center drawer, cyma scrolled apron, cabriole legs with pointed knees and scrolled knee brackets, beautifully sculptured claw and ball feet, original brasses and mellow light brown patina, Salem, Massachusetts, circa 1760-1780. In the finest state of preservation. Illustrated "Fine Points of Furniture, Early American" page 197.

Ht. 31″ Wd. 36″ Dp. 18½″

P3921 Chippendale mahogany blockfront bureau, finely sculptured claw and ball feet with swept back talons, scrolled center pendant, graduated drawers with round blocking retaining the original pine tree brasses, escutcheons, and side carry handles, Boston, Massachusetts, or vicinity, circa 1760-1780. The original warm golden brown patina, the undisturbed original condition and aspect of this bureau will satisfy the most discriminating connoisseur. This bureau formerly belonged to Mrs. Bradlee Smith of Brookline, Massachusetts, a direct descendant of William Penn.

Ht. 33¼″ Wd. 38″ Dp. 21¾″

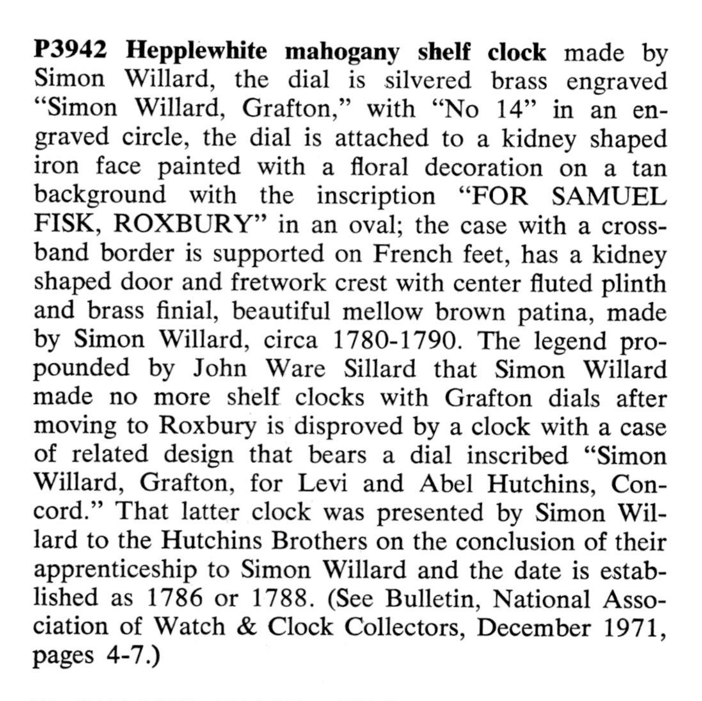

P3942 Hepplewhite mahogany shelf clock made by Simon Willard, the dial is silvered brass engraved "Simon Willard, Grafton," with "No 14" in an engraved circle, the dial is attached to a kidney shaped iron face painted with a floral decoration on a tan background with the inscription "FOR SAMUEL FISK, ROXBURY" in an oval; the case with a crossband border is supported on French feet, has a kidney shaped door and fretwork crest with center fluted plinth and brass finial, beautiful mellow brown patina, made by Simon Willard, circa 1780-1790. The legend propounded by John Ware Sillard that Simon Willard made no more shelf clocks with Grafton dials after moving to Roxbury is disproved by a clock with a case of related design that bears a dial inscribed "Simon Willard, Grafton, for Levi and Abel Hutchins, Concord." That latter clock was presented by Simon Willard to the Hutchins Brothers on the conclusion of their apprenticeship to Simon Willard and the date is established as 1786 or 1788. (See Bulletin, National Association of Watch & Clock Collectors, December 1971, pages 4-7.)

Ht. 34½″ Wd. 12½″ Dp. 5¾″

P3970 Hepplewhite mahogany half high or "grandmother" clock made and inscribed on the dial "Warranted by Joshua Wilder, Hingham (Mass.)" circa 1821. A contemporary inscription inside the case reads "Manufactured for Martin Fearing by Joshua Wilder 1821." The case is more sophisticated than the usual Wilder product and is in superb intact condition retaining the original fretwork, brass finials and nut brown finish. The inset quarter columns, crossbanded borders of waist and base panel, and the exemplary proportions are features seldom seen in this rare group of prized miniature clocks. A similar clock by this maker is in the Henry F. du Pont Winterthur Museum. Illustrated "Federal Furniture" Montgomery plate 149.

Ex Collection the late Mitchel Taradash.

Ht. 4′ 2¾″ Wd. 10⅞″ Dp. 5½″

P3995 Queen Anne cherry desk on frame in two sections, the original frame with finely scrolled apron, cabriole legs with straightish knees ending in platformed pad feet, one drawer in upper case section, original brasses with crescent cutouts, the interior with five drawers and pigeonholes, the desk has a fine undisturbed aspect with an old or original finish, Connecticut circa 1750-1760.

Ht. 40″ Wd. 36″ Dp. 18¾″ Wr. Lvl-27½″

P3959 Chippendale walnut mirror of important size, scrolled crest and base, large gilt pierced shell silhouetted in crest, carved and gilded mirror border, golden brown patina, Philadelphia or English circa 1750-1760.

This mirror was purchased from direct descendants of David Deshler, whose residence in Germantown, Pennsylvania, was occupied by George Washington.

Ht. 47″ Wd. 24½″

P3919 Chippendale San Domingan mahogany oxbow bureau, ogee bracket feet, the drawer fronts and top show finely figured grain, bronze patina, the backboard bears the contemporary chalk inscription "Emmons," ascribed to Thomas Emmons, Boston, Massachusetts, circa 1770-1780. Thomas Emmons was at one time in partnership with James Cogswell.

Ht. 31″ Wd. 37½′ Dr. 21¼″

P3986 Mahogany and gilt banjo clock retaining the original eglomise glass door and waist panels, both panels deep crimson with gilt borders in white background, the door panel centered by a gilt drapery, the waist panel floral, gilt moulded borders and original acorn finial, attributed to Aaron Willard, Jr., Boston, Massachusetts, circa 1820-1830. While unsigned the clock exhibits the identical painting to an Aaron Willard, Jr., banjo clock in Sack Brochure #17, #1271, page 540.

Ht. 33″ Wd. 10″ Dp. 3½″

P3996 Classical mahogany lighthouse clock, based on Eddystone lighthouse, invented and patented by Simon Willard. This example is in superb condition, retaining the original blown glass dome. The brass of the frontal cornucopia and laurel wreath mount, the ball feet, the chased dial and case borders and the bell finial retain the original fire gilding; the enamelled dial is inscribed "SIMON WILLARD & SON'S—PATENT." Made by Simon Willard & Son, Roxbury, Massachusetts, circa 1822-1830.

This clock was purchased from the Baum estate. Livermore Falls, Maine.

Ht. 30″ Dia. 8¼″

P3992 Chippendale mahogany oxbow bureau with blocked ends, ogee bracket feet, bale brasses, beautiful amber patina, Massachusetts circa 1760-1780. The bureau is exceptional in its compact proportions and bold serpentine outline.

Ht. 29¼″ Wd. 36½″ Dp. 21¾″

P3918 Chippendale mahogany side chair, cabriole legs with acanthus carved knees, claw and ball feet, twin arched apron with C-scrolled border and carved center, interlaced splat with silhouetted hearts, crest rail with scrolled border and carved ears, mellow light brown patina, school of James Gillingham, Philadelphia circa 1760-1780.

Ht. 39″

P3936 Queen Anne walnut corner chair, horseshoe seat, cabriole front leg with shell and bellflower carved knee and high ridged claw and ball foot, turned side and rear legs ending in pad feet, turned cross stretchers, vase shaped splats, mellow brown patina, Newport, Rhode Island, circa 1740-1760.

Ht. 31¼″ Wd. 29″

P3951 Queen Anne maple tripod tip table with burl veneered octagonal top, urn turned column, Massachusetts circa 1740-1760. The richly figured burl veneer with banded border relates to the early Queen Anne group of Massachusetts highboys and lowboys. To our knowledge its use on a candlestand is unique.

Ht. 27½″ Top 18″ × 18¼″

P3954 Chippendale walnut mirror with scrolled crest and base, carved and gilded pierced shell in crest with vine tracery, American or English circa 1760-1770. The mirror retains the original bevelled glass and back with four generations of family history recorded on the backboard. The oldest inscription reads: "This glass was given to Edward Packard in 1819 by this grandfather Frederick Sheldon who died in 1825 . . . who had it given to him on his marriage two years before by his father. Signed Edward Packard Aug. 18, 1827 Providence, R.I."

Ht. 44″ Wd. 24½″

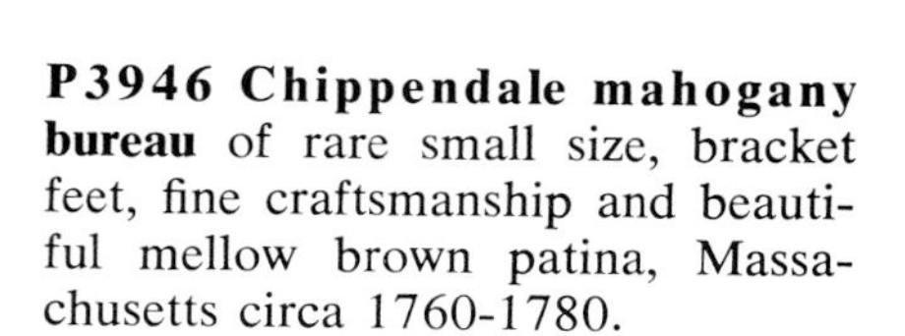
P3946 Chippendale mahogany bureau of rare small size, bracket feet, fine craftsmanship and beautiful mellow brown patina, Massachusetts circa 1760-1780.

Ht. 29½″ Wd. 36″ Dp. 19½″

P3905 and P3947 Two Sheraton mahogany end tables, ocatgonal tops with broad cross-banded top borders and rounded edges, ring turned turrets supported by bulbous reeded legs; each table fronted by two drawers, one with birdseye maple fronts, the other with curly maple fronts; Massachusetts circa 1800-1810. The tables were obviously made by the same craftsman and will serve as excellent companions.

P3905 Ht. 28½″ Top 22″ x 17¾″

P3947 Ht. 29¾″ Top 21½″ x 16¾″

P3912 Pair of Sheraton mahogany side chairs, drapery carved splats, egg and dart carved crest panel, tapered line inlaid legs which splay forward at the base, fine quality and condition, Philadelphia circa 1800-1810.

Ht. 34″

P3993 Hepplewhite mahogany inlaid writing desk in two sections, lower case with one long drawer with crossbanded and inlaid border, recessed tambour compartment below with turret corners, the tapered legs and stiles have birdseye maple panels in inlaid borders, the upper case with two crossbanded inlaid doors enclosing drawers and pigeonholes, choice mellow brown patina, bears the original label of Mark Pitman, Essex Street, Salem, Massachusetts, circa 1790-1810.

Ht. 52¼″ Wd. 38¼″ Dp. 19″

Wrtg. Lvl. 30½″

P3948 Sheraton mahogany armchair, the drapery carved splat and egg and dart carved crest panel are typical of one of the finest designs identified with Philadelphia Federal chairs; the serpentine arms end in carved rosettes, moulded tapered legs, stretchers, Philadelphia circa 1800-1810.

Ht. 36″ Wd. 22″

P3968 Pair of Classical mahogany harp back side chairs, the harp motif is a rare and brillant variation from the more typical lyre splat, the integration of the assymetrical harp into the design is a tour de force that could be attempted only by a master such as Duncan Phyfe; the crotch veneered crest panels and hairy paw feet relate to chairs of Phyfe's handiwork, choice bronze patina, attributed to Duncan Phyfe, New York circa 1810-1820. We know of two other pairs of this form. One pair is illustrated in the Girl Scout Loan catalogue #797 and a second pair is in the Henry F. du Pont Winterthur Museum, illustrated "Federal Furniture" Charles F. Montgomery, plate #74. Ex Collection the late Mitchel Taradash. Illustrated ANTIQUES January 1953, page 44 Illustrated "Living with Antiques" by Alice Winchester, page 90.

Ht. 32¼"

P3932 Sheraton mahogany sewing table, rectangular case with canted corners, ring turned turret columns, tapered reeded legs, two drawers and sewing slide, thin top with twin reeded edge, fine bronze patina, Salem, Massachusetts, circa 1800-1810.

Ht. 30″ Wd. 19¾″ Dp. 14¾″

P3945 Classical mahogany lyre back armchair, the chair is a classic model of the form usually ascribed to Duncan Phyfe with the acanthus carved lyre, hairy paw feet and rectangular crotch veneered crest panel; the reeded arms join the reeded seat members in a scrolled flourish, attributed to Duncan Phyfe, New York circa 1810-1820.

Ht. 32¼″ Wd. 19″

P3988 Sheraton mahogany and flame satinwood card table, bowed front and sides with turret ends, reeded legs, the frame has richly figured satinwood veneered panels, the three panelled front is centered by an oval, the top is also bordered by flame satinwood banding, fine old patina, Massachusetts circa 1800-1810.

Ht. 30″ Wd. 36″ Dp. 17¾″

P3913 Sheraton mahogany and flame satinwood end table with gallery, two drawers with finely matched flame satinwood fronts and crossbanded borders, turret ends with reeded columns supporting a shelf with wavy border, ring turned bulbous legs, fine mellow color, Salem, Massachusetts, circa 1800-1810.

Ht. 30½″ Wd. 18¾″ Dp. 17½″

P2565 Hepplewhite cherry tripod tilt top candlestand, octagonal top inlaid with a diamond center panel and with borders of black and white diagonals, reeded urn column, bowed legs with black and white diamond inlay ending in spade feet with diagonal inlay, choice amber patina, Massachusetts circa 1780-1800.

Ht. 27″ Top 21″ x 14″

P4006 Chippendale mahogany bow front bureau with classical influence, expressed brilliantly in the original Bilsted enamel handles, each view different, fluted quarter columns, moulded edge top with retaining moulding, fine quality and color, Philadelphia circa 1770-1790.

Ht. 36¼″ Wd. 43½″ Dp. 24¼″

P3965 Chippendale mahogany wing chair, square moulded legs and stretchers with a fine old finish, boldly serpentine wings and crest, nicely raked profile, Massachusetts circa 1760-1780.

Ht. 46½″ Wd. 32½″ Dp. 32¼″

P4009 Chippendale mahogany marlborough foot bed, fluted tapering foot posts, square tapering head posts, original rails and pine headboard with double arched crest, choice mellow brown patina, Rhode Island circa 1760-1780. The foot-posts above the capitals and corresponding sections of the head-posts have been pieced.

Ht. 6′ 11″ Lg. 76½″ Wd. 56¾″

P4008 Chippendale mahogany serpentine front bureau with blocked ends, ogee bracket feet, the fronts and top feature finely figured crotch grain, fine mellow brown patina, Massachusetts circa 1760-1780.

Ht. 30½″ Wd. 37½″ Dp. 21″

P4007 Hepplewhite bowfront bureau with mahogany veneered fronts, birch top and sides, tall French feet, scrolled apron centered by inlaid sunburst, the drawers and apron have curly maple borders, original chased brasses, a choice nut brown patina enhances the beauty of the front, Portsmouth, New Hampshire, circa 1780-1800.

Ht. 36′ Wd. 41″ Dp. 21¼″

P3994 Classical mahogany library or sofa table, drop leaves with rounded ends, the case supported by hexagonal panelled columns and a horizontal stretcher with hexagonal panels meeting in a turned center with concentric ring turned terminals, acanthus carved and moulded legs ending in carved paw castered feet, choice color and quality, attributed to Duncan Phyfe, New York circa 1820-1825. The attribution to Duncan Phyfe is based on the distinctive hexagonal columns appearing on a secretary bearing Phyfe's label and a card table made by Duncan Phyfe for John Jacob Astor—see McClelland "Duncan Phyfe" plates 239 and 251.

Ht. 28⅝″ Wd. 26½″ Lg. 39″

P4001 Classical mahogany piano stool, the chair back has moulded stiles, horizontal splat with medallion carved center panelled crest; the chair swivels on turned column, acanthus carved knees, carved paw feet, New York circa 1810-1825.

Ht. 34½″

P4005 Hepplewhite mahogany glass door secretary, the glass doors with inlaid mullions of astragal design, the butler's desk compartment reveals an exceptional interior with urn inlay motif on center door, the pigeonhole brackets have etched designs in color, that treatment repeated on the top border of the lower case; under the desk section are cupboard doors with inlaid borders, French feet and scrolled apron, Baltimore or Annapolis, Maryland, circa 1780-1800.

Ht. 8′1″ Wd. 48½″ Dp. 21¾″

INDEX

By Donald R. Sack, Israel Sack, Inc., New York

This Index is for Volume Four

This index has been arranged in five ways:

First: Form: Items listed alphabetically and also listed in period. Example: Chairs — Pilgrim, William & Mary, etc.

Second: Regional: Items listed by location. Example: New York: Bureaus, Chairs, etc. Also large states such as Massachusetts have centers within them listed separately.

Third: Cabinetmakers: Listed in alphabetical order.

Fourth: Clockmakers: Listed in alphabetical order.

Fifth: Silversmiths and Painters: Listed in alphabetical order.

Each item is listed by p for page number and item number following the page number in the catalog. Example: p. 100, *68*.

Also in the index, where the craftsman is known, the name is preceded by page number and item number.